People

People

AN ANTHOLOGY OF READINGS

Selected by Jane Syburg

FIDES PUBLISHERS, INC.
NOTRE DAME, INDIANA

Library of Congress Catalog Card Number: 68-15362

Preface

The stories and poems in *People* were selected to illustrate and elaborate on two basic themes: people in relationship to other people and people in relationship to God.

The works from Chekhov's "Lament" to the biblical excerpts explore the everyday interpersonal associations the average person has. The first two stories point up the general theme of interdependence and the following works explore the various kinds of relationships in some detail.

The second section, beginning with Thomas Wolfe's "The Far and the Near," delves into man's view of his god, sometimes showing a need for a supreme being and other times exploring the consequences of belief.

The works were not selected because they answer the basic questions of human experience but because they raise them and make exploration somewhat more orderly.

January, 1968 JANE SYBURG

Contents

PART I

PART II

Contents

PART I

PART II

PART I

ANTON CHEKHOV

The Lament

It is twilight. A thick wet snow is slowly twirling around the newly lighted street lamps, and lying in soft thin layers on roofs, on horses' backs, on people's shoulders and hats. The cabdriver Iona Potapov is quite white, and looks like a phantom; he is bent double as far as a human body can bend double; he is seated on his box; he never makes a move. If a whole snowdrift fell on him, it seems as if he would not find it necessary to shake it off. His little horse is also quite white, and remains motionless; its immobility, its angularity, and its straight wooden-looking legs, even close by, give it the appearance of a gingerbread horse worth a *kopek*. It is, no doubt, plunged in deep thought. If you were snatched from the plow, from your usual gray surroundings, and were thrown into this slough full of monstrous lights, unceasing noise, and hurrying people, you too would find it difficult not to think.

Iona and his little horse have not moved from their place for a long while. They left their yard before dinner, and up to now, not a fare. The evening mist is descending over the town, the white lights of the lamps replacing brighter rays, and the hubbub of the street getting louder. "Cabby for Viborg way!" suddenly hears Iona. "Cabby!"

Iona jumps, and through his snow-covered eyelashes sees an officer in a greatcoat, with his hood over his head.

"Viborg way!" the officer repeats. "Are you asleep, eh? Viborg way!"

With a nod of assent Iona picks up the reins, in consequence of which layers of snow slip off the horse's back and neck. The officer seats himself in the sleigh, the cabdriver smacks his lips to encourage his horse, stretches out his neck like a swan, sits up, and, more from habit than necessity, brandishes his whip. The little horse also stretches its neck, bends its wooden-looking legs, and makes a move undecidedly.

"What are you doing, werewolf!" is the exclamation Iona hears from the dark mass moving to and fro, as soon as they have started.

"Where the devil are you going? To the r-r-right!"

"You do not know how to drive. Keep to the right!" calls the officer angrily.

A coachman from a private carriage swears at him; a passerby, who has run across the road and rubbed his shoulder against the horse's nose, looks at him furiously as he sweeps the snow from his sleeve. Iona shifts about on his seat as if he were on needles, moves his elbows as if he were trying to keep his equilibrium, and gapes about like someone suffocating, who does not understand why and wherefore he is there.

"What scoundrels they all are!" jokes the officer; "one would think they had all entered into an agreement to jostle you or fall under your horse."

Iona looks round at the officer, and moves his lips. He evidently wants to say something, but the only sound that issues is a snuffle.

"What?" asks the officer.

Iona twists his mouth into a smile, and with an effort says hoarsely:

"My son, *barin,* died this week."

"Hm! What did he die of?"

Iona turns with his whole body toward his fare, and says:

"And who knows! They say high fever. He was three days in

the hospital, and then died. . . . God's will be done."

"Turn round! The devil!" sounds from the darkness. "Have you popped off, old doggie, eh? Use your eyes!"

"Go on, go on," says the officer, "otherwise we shall not get there by tomorrow. Hurry up a bit!"

The cabdriver again stretches his neck, sits up, and, with a bad grace, brandishes his whip. Several times again he turns to look at his fare, but the latter has closed his eyes, and apparently is not disposed to listen. Having deposited the officer in the Viborg, he stops by the tavern, doubles up on his seat, and again remains motionless, while the snow once more begins to cover him and his horse. An hour, and another. . . . Then, along the footpath, with a squeak of galoshes, and quarreling, come three young men, two of them tall and lanky, the third one short and humpbacked.

"Cabby, to the Police Bridge!" in a cracked voice calls the humpback. "The three of us for two *griveniks!*"

Iona picks up his reins, and smacks his lips. Two *griveniks* is not a fair price, but he does not mind whether it is a *rouble* or five *kopeks*—to him it is all the same now, so long as they are fares. The young men, jostling each other and using bad language, approach the sleigh, and all three at once try to get onto the seat; then begins a discussion as to which two shall sit and who shall be the one to stand. After wrangling, abusing each other, and much petulance, it is at last decided that the humpback shall stand, as he is the smallest.

"Now then, hurry up!" says the humpback in a twanging voice, as he takes his place and breathes on Iona's neck. "Old furry! Here, mate, what a cap you have! There is not a worse one to be found in all Petersburg! . . ."

"He-he! — he-he!" giggles Iona. "Such a . . ."

"Now you, 'such a,' hurry up, are you going the whole way at this pace? Are you? . . . Do you want it in the neck?"

"My head feels like bursting," says one of the lanky ones. "Last night at the Donkmasovs, Vaska and I drank the whole of four bottles of cognac."

"I don't understand what you lie for," says the other lanky

one angrily; "you lie like a brute."

"God strike me, it's the truth!"

"It's as much the truth as that a louse coughs!"

"He, he," grins Iona, "what gay young gentlemen!"

"Pshaw, go to the devil!" says the humpback indignantly. "Are you going to get on or not, you old pest? Is that the way to drive! Use the whip a bit! Go on, devil, go on, give it to him well!"

Iona feels at his back the little man wriggling, and the tremble in his voice. He listens to the insults hurled at him, sees the people, and little by little the feeling of loneliness leaves him. The humpback goes on swearing until he gets mixed up in some elaborate six-foot oath, or chokes with coughing. The lankies begin to talk about a certain Nadejda Petrovna. Iona looks round at them several times; he waits for a temporary silence, then, turning round again, he murmurs:

"My son . . . died this week."

"We must all die," sighs the humpback, wiping his lips after an attack of coughing. "Now, hurry up, hurry up! Gentlemen, I really cannot go any farther like this! When will he get us there?"

"Well, just you stimulate him a little in the neck!"

"You old pest, do you hear, I'll bone your neck for you! If one treated the likes of you with ceremony one would have to go on foot! Do you hear, old serpent Gorinytch! Or do you not care a spit?"

Iona hears rather than feels the blows they deal him.

"He, he," he laughs. "They are gay young gentlemen, God bless 'em!"

"Cabby, are you married?" asks a lanky one.

"I? He, he, gay young gentlemen! Now I have only a wife and the moist ground . . . he, ho, ho . . . that is to say, the grave. My son has died, and I am alive. . . . A wonderful thing, death mistook the door . . . instead of coming to me, it went to my son. . . ."

Iona turns round to tell them how his son died, but at this moment, the humpback, giving a little sigh, announces, "Thank

God, we have at last reached our destination," and Iona watches them disappear through the dark entrance. Once more he is alone, and again surrounded by silence. . . . His grief, which has abated for a short while, returns and rends his heart with greater force. With an anxious and hurried look, he searches among the crowds passing on either side of the street to find whether there may be just one person who will listen to him. But the crowds hurry by without noticing him or his trouble. Yet it is such an immense, illimitable grief. Should his heart break and the grief pour out, it would flow over the whole earth, so it seems, and yet no one sees it. It has managed to conceal itself in such an insignificant shell that no one can see it even by day and with a light.

Iona sees a hall porter with some sacking, and decides to talk to him.

"Friend, what sort of time is it?" he asks.

"Past nine. What are you standing here for? Move on."

Iona moves on a few steps, doubles himself up, and abandons himself to his grief. He sees it is useless to turn to people for help. In less than five minutes he straightens himself, holds up his head as if he felt some sharp pain, and gives a tug at the reins; he can bear it no longer. "The stables," he thinks, and the little horse, as if it understands, starts off at a trot.

About an hour and a half later Iona is seated by a large dirty stove. Around the stove, on the floor, on the benches, people are snoring; the air is thick and suffocatingly hot. Iona looks at the sleepers, scratches himself, and regrets having returned so early.

"I have not even earned my fodder," he thinks. "That's what's my trouble. A man who knows his job, who has had enough to eat, and his horse too, can always sleep peacefully."

A young cabdriver in one of the corners half gets up, grunts sleepily, and stretches towards a bucket of water.

"Do you want a drink?" Iona asks him.

"Don't I want a drink?"

"That's so? Your good health! But listen, mate — you know, my son is dead. . . . Did you hear? This week, in the hospital. . . . It's a long story."

Iona looks to see what effect his words have, but sees none — the young man has hidden his face and is fast asleep again. The old man sighs, and scratches his head. Just as much as the young one wants to drink, the old man wants to talk. It will soon be a week since his son died, and he has not been able to speak about it properly to anyone. One must tell it slowly and carefully; how his son fell ill, how he suffered, what he said before he died, how he died. One must describe every detail of the funeral, and the journey to the hospital to fetch the dead son's clothes. His daughter Anissia has remained in the village — one must talk about her too. Is it nothing he has to tell? Surely the listener would gasp and sigh, and sympathize with him? It is better, too, to talk to women; although they are stupid, two words are enough to make them sob.

"I'll go and look after my horse," thinks Iona; "there's always time to sleep. No fear of that!"

He puts on his coat, and goes to the stables to his horse; he thinks of the corn, the hay, the weather. When he is alone, he dares not think of his son; he can speak about him to anyone, but to think of him, and picture him to himself, is unbearably painful.

"Are you tucking in?" Iona asks his horse, looking at its bright eyes; "go on, tuck in, though we've not earned our corn, we can eat hay. Yes! I am too old to drive — my son could have, not I. He was a first-rate cabdriver. If only he had lived!"

Iona is silent for a moment, then continues:

"That's how it is, my old horse. There's no more Kuzma Ionitch. He has left us to live, and he went off pop. Now let's say, you had a foal, you were the foal's mother, and suddenly, let's say, that foal went and left you to live after him. It would be sad, wouldn't it?"

The little horse munches, listens, and breathes over its master's hand. . . .

Iona's feelings are too much for him, and he tells the little horse the whole story.

IRWIN SHAW

Dry Rock

"We're late," Helen said, as the cab stopped at a light. "We're twenty minutes late." She looked at her husband accusingly.

"All right," Fitzsimmons said. "I couldn't help it. The work was on the desk and it had to . . ."

"This is the one dinner party of the year I didn't want to be late for," Helen said. "So naturally . . ."

The cab started and was halfway across the street when the Ford sedan roared into it, twisting, with a crashing and scraping of metal, a high mournful scream of brakes, the tinkling of glass. The cab shook a little, then subsided.

The cabby, a little gray man, turned and looked back worriedly. "Everybody is all right?" he asked nervously.

"Everybody is fine," Helen said bitterly, pulling at her cape to get it straight again after the jolting.

"No damage done," said Fitzsimmons, smiling reassuringly at the cabby, who looked very frightened.

"I am happy to hear that," the cabby said. He got out of his car and stood looking sadly at his fender, now thoroughly crumpled, and his headlight, now without a lens. The door of the Ford opened and its driver sprang out. He was a large young man with a light gray hat. He glanced hurriedly at the cab.

"Why don't yuh watch where the hell yer goin?" he asked harshly.

"The light was in my favor," said the cabby. He was a small man of fifty, in a cap and ragged coat, and he spoke with a heavy accent. "It turned green and I started across. I would like your license, Mister."

"What for?" the man in the gray hat shouted. "Yer load's all right. Get on yer way. No harm done." He started back to his car.

The cabby gently put his hand on the young man's arm. "Excuse me, friend," he said. "It is a five-dollar job, at least. I would like to see your license."

The young man pulled his arm away, glared at the cabby. "Aaah," he said and swung. His fist made a loud, surprising noise against the cabby's nose. The old man sat down slowly on the running board of his cab, holding his head wearily in his hands. The young man in the gray hat stood over him, bent over, fists still clenched. "Didn't I tell yuh no harm was done?" he shouted. "Why didn't yuh lissen t' me? I got a good mind to . . ."

"Now, see here," Fitzsimmons said, opening the rear door and stepping out.

"What d'*you* want?" The young man turned and snarled at Fitzsimmons, his fists held higher. "Who asked for *you*?"

"I saw the whole thing," Fitzsimmons began, "and I don't think you . . ."

"Aaah," snarled the young man. "Dry up."

"Claude," Helen called. "Claude, keep out of this."

"Claude," the young man repeated balefully. "Dry up, Claude."

"Are you all right?" Fitzsimmons asked, bending over the cabby, who still sat reflectively on the running board, his head down, his old and swollen cap hiding his face, blood trickling down his clothes.

"I'm all right," the cabby said wearily. He stood up, looked wonderingly at the young man. "Now, my friend, you force me to make trouble. Police!" he called, loudly. *"Police!"*

"Say, lissen," the man in the gray hat shouted. "What the hell do yuh need to call the cops for? Hey, cut it out!"

"Police!" the old cabby shouted calmly, but with fervor deep in his voice. "Police!"

"I ought to give it to yuh good." The young man shook his fist under the cabby's nose. He jumped around nervously. "This is a small matter," he shouted, "nobody needs the cops!"

"Police!" called the cabby.

"Claude," Helen put her head out the window. "Let's get out of here and let the two gentlemen settle this any way they please."

"I apologize!" The young man held the cabby by his lapels with both large hands, shook him, to emphasize his apology. "Excuse me. I'm sorry. Stop yelling police," he shouted.

"I'm going to have you locked up," the cabby said. He stood there, slowly drying the blood off his shabby coat with his cap. His hair was gray, but long and full, like a musician's. He had a big head for his little shoulders, and a sad, lined little face and he looked older than fifty, to Fitzsimmons, and very poor, neglected, badly nourished. "You have committed a crime," the cabby said, "and there is a punishment for it."

"Will yuh talk to him?" The young man turned savagely to Fitzsimmons. "Will yuh tell him I'm sorry?"

"It's entirely up to him," Fitzsimmons said.

"We're a half hour late," Helen announced bitterly. "The perfect dinner guests."

"It is not enough to be sorry," said the cab driver. *"Police . . ."*

"Say, listen, Bud," the young man said, his voice quick and confidential, "what's yer name?"

"Leopold Tarloff," the cabby said. "I have been driving a cab on the streets of New York for twenty years, and everybody thinks just because you're a cab driver they can do whatever they want to you."

"Lissen, Leopold," the young man pushed his light gray hat far back on his head. "Let's be sensible. I hit yer cab. All right. I hit you. All right."

"What's all right about it?" Tarloff asked.

"What I mean is, I admit it, I confess I did it, that's what I mean. All right." The young man grabbed Tarloff's short ragged arms as he spoke, intensely. "Why the fuss? It happens every day. Police are unnecessary. I'll tell yuh what I'll do with yuh, Leopold. Five dollars, yuh say, for the fender. All right. And for the bloody nose, another pound. What do yuh say? Everybody is satisfied. Yuh've made yerself a fiver on the transaction; these good people go to their party without no more delay."

Tarloff shook his arms free from the huge hands of the man in the gray hat. He put his head back and ran his fingers through his thick hair and spoke coldly. "I don't want to hear another word. I have never been so insulted in my whole life."

The young man stepped back, his arms wide, palms up wonderingly. "I insult him!" He turned to Fitzsimmons. "Did you hear me insult this party?" he asked.

"Claude!" Helen called. "Are we going to sit here all night?"

"A man steps up and hits me in the nose," Tarloff said. "He thinks he makes everything all right with five dollars. He is mistaken. Not with five hundred dollars."

"How much d'yuh think a clap in the puss is worth?" the young man growled. "Who d'yuh think y'are — Joe Louis?"

"Not ten thousand dollars," Tarloff said, on the surface calm, but quivering underneath. "Not for twenty thousand dollars. My dignity."

"His dignity!"

"What do you want to do?" Fitzsimmons asked, conscious of Helen glooming in the rear seat of the cab.

"I would like to take him to the station house and make a complaint," Tarloff said. "You would have to come with me, if you'd be so kind. What is your opinion on the matter?"

"Will yuh tell him the cops are not a necessity!" the young man said hoarsely. "Will yuh tell the bum?"

"Claude!" called Helen.

"It's up to you," Fitzsimmons said, looking with what he hoped was an impartial, judicious expression at Tarloff, hoping he wouldn't have to waste any more time. "You do what you think you ought to do."

Tarloff smiled, showing three yellow teeth in the front of his small and childlike mouth, curved and red and surprising in the lined and weather-beaten old hackie's face. "Thank you very much," he said. "I am glad to see you agree with me."

Fitzsimmons sighed.

"Yer drivin' me crazy!" the young man shouted at Tarloff. "Yer makin' life impossible!"

"To you," Tarloff said with dignity, "I talk from now on only in a court of law. That's my last word."

The young man stood there, breathing heavily, his fists clenching and unclenching, his pale gray hat shining in the light of a street lamp. A policeman turned the corner, walking in a leisurely and abstract manner, his eyes on the legs of a girl across the street.

Fitzsimmons went over to him. "Officer," he said, "there's a little job for you over here." The policeman regretfully took his eyes off the girl's legs and sighed and walked slowly over to where the two cars were still nestling against each other.

"What are yuh?" the young man was asking Tarloff, when Fitzsimmons came up with the policeman. "Yuh don't act like an American citizen. What are yuh?"

"I'm a Russian," Tarloff said. "But I'm in the country twenty-five years now, I know what the rights of an individual are."

"Yeah," said the young man hopelessly. "Yeah . . ."

The Fitzsimmonses drove silently to the police station in the cab, with Tarloff driving slowly and carefully, though with hands that shook on the wheel. The policeman drove with the young man in the young man's Ford. Fitzsimmons saw the Ford stop at the cigar store and the young man jump out and go into the store, into a telephone booth.

"For three months," Helen said, as they drove, "I've been trying to get Adele Lowrie to invite us to dinner. Now we've finally managed it. Perhaps we ought to call her and invite the whole party down to night court."

"It isn't night court," Fitzsimmons said patiently. "It's a police station. And I think you might take it a little better. After all, the poor old man has no one else to speak up for him."

"Leopold Tarloff," Helen said. "It sounds impossible. Leopold Tarloff. Leopold Tarloff."

They sat in silence until Tarloff stopped the cab in front of the police station and opened the door for them. The Ford with the policeman and the young man drove up right behind them and they all went in together.

There were some people up in front of the desk lieutenant, a dejected-looking man with long mustaches and a loud, blonde woman who kept saying that the man had threatened her with a baseball bat three times that evening. Two Negroes with bloody bandages around their heads were waiting, too.

"It will take some time," said the policeman. "There are two cases ahead of you. My name is Kraus."

"Oh, my," said Helen.

"You'd better call Adele," Fitzsimmons said. "Tell her not to hold dinner for us."

Helen held her hand out gloomily for nickels.

"I'm sorry," Tarloff said anxiously, "to interrupt your plans for the evening."

"Perfectly all right," Fitzsimmons said, trying to screen his wife's face from Tarloff by bending over to search for the nickels in his pocket.

Helen went off, disdainfully holding her long formal skirt up with her hand, as she walked down the spit- and butt-marked corridor of the police station toward a pay telephone. Fitzsimmons reflectively watched her elegant back retreat down the hallway.

"I am tired," Tarloff said. "I think I will have to sit down, if you will excuse me." He sat on the floor, looking up with a frail, apologetic smile on his red face worn by wind and rain and traffic policemen. Fitzsimmons suddenly felt like crying, watching the old man sitting there among the spit and cigarette butts, on the floor against the wall, with his cap off and his great bush of musician's gray hair giving the lie to the tired, weathered face below it.

Four men threw open the outside doors and walked into the police station with certainty and authority. They all wore the same light-gray hats with the huge flat brims. The young man who had hit Tarloff greeted them guardedly. "I'm glad you're here, Pidgear," he said to the man who, by some subtle mixture of stance and clothing, of lift of eyebrow and droop of mouth, announced himself as leader.

They talked swiftly and quietly in a corner.

"A Russian!" Pidgear's voice rang out angrily. "There are 10,000 cab drivers in the metropolitan area, you have to pick a Russian to punch in the nose!"

"I'm excitable!" the young man yelled. "Can I help it if I'm excitable? My father was the same way; it's a family characteristic."

"Go tell that to the Russian," Pidgear said. He went over to one of the three men who had come with him, a large man who needed a shave and whose collar was open at the throat, as though no collar could be bought large enough to go all the way around that neck. The large man nodded, went over to Tarloff still sitting patiently against the wall.

"You speak Russian?" the man with the open collar said to Tarloff.

"Yes, sir," Tarloff said.

The large man sat down slowly beside him, gripped Tarloff's knee confidentially in his tremendous hairy hand, spoke excitedly, winningly, in Russian.

Pidgear and the young man who had hit Tarloff came over to Fitzsimmons, leaving the other two men in the gray hats, small, dark men with shining eyes, who just stood at the door and looked hotly on.

"My name is Pidgear," the man said to Fitzsimmons, who by now was impressed with the beautiful efficiency of the system that had been put into motion by the young driver of the Ford — an obviously legal mind like Pidgear's, a man who spoke Russian, and two intense men with gray hats standing on call just to see justice done, and all collected in the space of fifteen minutes. "Alton Pidgear," the man said, smiling professionally at Fitzsimmons. "I represent Mr. Rusk."

"Yeah," said the young man.

"My name is Fitzsimmons."

"Frankly, Mr. Fitzsimmons," Pidgear said, "I would like to see you get Mr. Tarloff to call this whole thing off. It's an embarrassing affair for all concerned; nobody stands to gain anything by pressing it."

Helen came back and Fitzsimmons saw by the expression on her face that she wasn't happy. "They're at the soup by now," she said loudly to Fitzsimmons. "Adele said for us to take all the time we want, they're getting along fine."

"Mr. Rusk is willing to make a handsome offer," Pidgear said. "Five dollars for the car, five dollars for the nose . . ."

"Go out to dinner with your husband," Helen muttered, "and you wind up in a telephone booth in a police station. 'Excuse me for being late, darling, but I'm calling from the 8th precinct, this is our night for street fighting.' "

"Sssh, Helen, please," Fitzsimmons said. He hadn't eaten since nine that morning and his stomach was growling with hunger.

"It was all a mistake," Pidgear said smoothly. "A natural mistake. Why should the man be stubborn? He is being reimbursed for everything, isn't he? I wish you would talk to him, Mr. Fitzsimmons; we don't want to keep you from your social engagements. Undoubtedly," Pidgear said, eyeing their evening clothes respectfully, "you and the madam were going to an important dinner party. It would be too bad to spoil an important dinner party for a little thing like this. Why, this whole affair is niggling," he said, waving his hand in front of Fitzsimmons' face. "Absolutely niggling."

Fitzsimmons looked over to where Tarloff and the other Russian were sitting on the floor. From Tarloff's face and gestures, even though he was talking in deepest Russian, Fitzsimmons could tell Tarloff was still as firm as ever. Fitzsimmons looked closely at Rusk, who was standing looking at Tarloff through narrow, baleful eyes.

"Why're you so anxious?" Fitzsimmons asked.

Rusk's eyes clouded over and his throat throbbed against his collar with rage. "I don't want to appear in court!" he yelled.

"I don't want the whole damn business to start all over again, investigation, lawyers, fingerprints . . ."

Pidgear punched him savagely in the ribs, his fist going a short distance, but with great violence.

"Why don't you buy time on the National Broadcasting System?" Pidgear asked. "Make an address, coast to coast!"

Rusk glared murderously for a moment at Pidgear, then leaned over toward Fitzsimmons, pointing a large blunt finger at him. "Do I have to put my finger in your mouth?" he whispered hoarsely.

"What does he mean by that?" Helen asked loudly. "Put his finger in your mouth? Why should he put his finger in your mouth?"

Rusk looked at her with complete hatred, turned, too full for words, and stalked away, with Pidgear after him. The two little men in the gray hats watched the room without moving.

"Claude?" Helen began.

"Obviously," Fitzsimmons said, his voice low, "Mr. Rusk isn't anxious for anyone to look at his fingerprints. He's happier this way."

"You picked a fine night!" Helen shook her head sadly. "Why can't we just pick up and get out of here?"

Rusk, with Pidgear at his side, strode back. He stopped in front of the Fitzsimmonses. "I'm a family man," he said, trying to sound like one. "I ask yuh as a favor. Talk to the Russian."

"I had to go to Bergdorf Goodman," Helen said, too deep in her own troubles to bother with Rusk, "to get a gown to spend the evening in a police station. 'Mrs. Claude Fitzsimmons was lovely last night in blue velvet and silver fox at Officer Kraus' reception at the 8th precinct. Other guests were the well-known Leopold Tarloff, and the Messrs. Pidgear and Rusk, in gray hats. Other guests included the Russian ambassador and two leading Italian artillerymen, also in gray hats.' "

Pidgear laughed politely. "Your wife is a very witty woman," he said.

"Yes," said Fitzsimmons, wondering why he'd married her.

"Will yuh just *ask*?" Rusk demanded. "Can it hurt yuh?"

"We're willing to do our part," Pidgear said. "We even brought down a Russian to talk to him and clear up any little points in his own language. No effort is too great."

Fitzsimmons' stomach growled loudly. "Haven't eaten all day," he said, embarrassed.

"That's what happens," Pidgear said. "Naturally."

"Yeah," said Rusk.

"Perhaps I should go out and get you a malted milk," Helen suggested coldly.

Fitzsimmons went over to where Tarloff was sitting with the other Russian. The others followed him.

"Are you sure, Mr. Tarloff," Fitzsimmons said, "that you still want to prosecute?"

"Yes," Tarloff said promptly.

"Ten dollars," Rusk said. "I offer yuh ten dollars. Can a man do more?"

"Money is not the object." With his cap Tarloff patted his nose, which was still bleeding slowly and had swelled enormously, making Tarloff look lopsided and monstrous.

"What's the object?" Rusk asked.

"The object, Mr. Rusk, is principle."

"*You* talk to him," Rusk said to Fitzsimmons.

"All right," Officer Kraus said, "you can go up there now."

They all filed in in front of the lieutenant sitting high at his desk.

Tarloff told his story, the accident, the wanton punch in the nose.

"It's true," Pidgear said, "that there was an accident, that there was a slight scuffle after by mistake. But the man isn't hurt. A little swelling in the region of the nose. No more." He pointed dramatically to Tarloff.

"Physically," Tarloff said, clutching his cap, talking with difficulty because his nose was clogged, "physically that's true. I am not badly hurt. But in a mental sense . . ." He shrugged. "I have suffered an injury."

"Mr. Rusk is offering the amount of ten dollars," Pidgear said. "Also, he apologizes; he's sorry."

The lieutenant looked wearily down at Rusk. "Are you sorry?" he asked.

"I'm sorry," said Rusk, raising his right hand. "On the Bible, I swear I'm sorry."

"Mr. Tarloff," the lieutenant said, "if you wish to press charges there are certain steps you will have to take. A deposition will have to be taken. Have you got witnesses?"

"Here," Tarloff said with a shy smile at the Fitzsimmonses.

"They will have to be present," the lieutenant said sleepily.

"Oh, great," Helen said.

"A warrant will have to be sworn out, there must be a hearing at which the witnesses must also be present . . ."

"Oh, great," Helen said.

"Then the trial," said the lieutenant.

"Great!" Helen said loudly.

"The question is, Mr. Tarloff," said the lieutenant, yawning, "are you willing to go through all that trouble?"

"The fact is," Tarloff said unhappily, "he hit me in the head without provocation. He is guilty of a crime on my person. He insulted me. He did me an injustice. The law exists for such things. One individual is not to be hit by another individual in the streets of the city without legal punishment." Tarloff was using his hands to try to get everyone, the Fitzsimmonses, the lieutenant, Pidgear, to understand. "There is a principle. The dignity of the human body. Justice. For a bad act a man suffers. It's an important thing . . ."

"I'm excitable," Rusk shouted. "If yuh want, yuh can hit me in the head."

"That is not the idea," Tarloff said.

"The man is sorry," the lieutenant said, wiping his eyes, "he is offering you the sum of ten dollars; it will be a long, hard job to bring this man to trial; it will cost a lot of the taxpayers' money; you are bothering these good people here who have other things to do. What is the sense in it, Mr. Tarloff?"

Tarloff scraped his feet slowly on the dirty floor, looked sadly, hopefully, at Fitzsimmons. Fitzsimmons looked at his wife, who was glaring at Tarloff, tapping her foot sharply again and again. Fitzsimmons looked back at Tarloff, standing there, before the high desk, small, in his ragged coat and wild gray hair, his little worn face twisted and grotesque with the swollen nose, his eyes lost and appealing. Fitzsimmons shrugged sadly. Tarloff drooped inside his old coat, shook his head wearily, shrugged, deserted once and for all before the lieutenant's desk, on the dry rock of principle.

"OK," he said.

"Here," Rusk brought the ten-dollar bill out with magical speed.

Tarloff pushed it away. "Get out of here," he said, without looking up.

No one talked all the way to Adele Lowrie's house. Tarloff opened the door and sat, looking straight ahead, while they got out. Helen went to the door of the house and rang. Silently, Fitzsimmons offered Tarloff the fare. Tarloff shook his head. "You have been very good," he said. "Forget it."

Fitzsimmons put the money away slowly.

"Claude!" Helen called. "The door's open."

Fitzsimmons hated his wife, suddenly, without turning to look at her. He put out his hand and Tarloff shook it wearily.

"I'm awfully sorry," Fitzsimmons said. "I wish I . . ."

Tarloff shrugged. "That's all right," he said. "I understand." His face, in the shabby light of the cab, worn and old and battered by the streets of the city, was a deep well of sorrow. "There is no time. Principle." He laughed, shrugged. "Today there is no time for anything."

He shifted gears and the taxi moved slowly off, its motor grinding noisily.

"Claude!" Helen called.

"Oh, shut up!" Fitzsimmons said as he turned and walked into Adele Lowrie's house.

W. H. AUDEN

The Unknown Citizen

To JS/07/M/378

THIS MARBLE MONUMENT IS ERECTED BY THE STATE

He was found by the Bureau of Statistics to be
One against whom there was no official complaint,
And all the reports on his conduct agree
That, in the modern sense of an old-fashioned word, he was a saint,
For in everything he did he served the Greater Community.
Except for the War till the day he retired
He worked in a factory and never got fired,
But satisfied his employers, Fudge Motors Inc.
Yet he wasn't a scab or odd in his views,
For his Union reports that he paid his dues,
(Our report on his Union shows it was sound)
And our Social Psychology workers found
That he was popular with his mates and liked a drink.

The Press are convinced that he bought a paper every day
And that his reactions to advertisements were normal in every way.
Policies taken out in his name prove that he was fully insured,
And his Health-card shows he was once in hospital but left it cured.
Both Producers Research and High-Grade Living declare
He was fully sensible to the advantages of the Installment Plan
and had everything necessary to the Modern Man,
A gramophone, a radio, a car and a frigidaire.
Our researchers into Public Opinion are content
That he held the proper opinions for the time of year;
When there was peace, he was for peace; when there
was war, he went.
He was married and added five children to the population,
Which our Eugenist says was the right number for a parent
of his generation,
And our teachers report that he never interfered with their education.
Was he free? Was he happy? The question is absurd;
Had anything been wrong, we should certainly have heard.

JOHN HOLMES

Your Kind of Joy

If you were born calm, then keep on calmly.
Every room you come into, come in slowly with a smile,
Calmly. Linger. Speak of the others who will be there
Next time, or in a little while.

If God made you to be angry, be angry.
For God's sake, if you hate a man, hurt him.
Hurry your errands. Shout. Curse. Blaze.
Try for a fiery good out of ashen days.
If a house rots, or a dog starves, or the law is absurd,
Show it. Never pocket a stone. Throw it.

And let the proud and plain and quiet
Be quiet and be proud
And never speak aloud.

Be old, if you are old, your age your own.
If you are tired in the world, or lost, or cold,
Howl till you are found and warm and fed
Or dead. A man said, Live life near the bone.

If you were born full of joy, if you love walking,
If you talk midnight down and bring in the dawn with music,
Branching day by day in the love of good companions,
Then go so.
If you breathe your own house, hear your books,
Wear time like the sun's brown on the back of your own hand,
If you think alone like the wind across your age,
Or see your country from ten thousand feet up in summer air,
Then go so. Be your joy.

Joy is an easy word to say,
But it cuts like hunger.
Joy was never most of any day,
But it lasts, like anger.

It is not too late now, ever or now. It is time,
Taking the world's night in one hand, and in one your light,
To mix them, mould them, burn, change them, cry
Your kind of joy, and know why.
Let women who teach children, women who love men,
Boys who use their bodies to climb cliffs and swim,
With living words make living real,
And men who speak color, think history, act in steel,
Or bend or break or build our earth against our weather,
Speak,
All the joyful all together.

STEVE ALLEN

The Secret

I didn't know I was dead until I walked into the bathroom and looked in the mirror.

In fact I didn't even know it at that exact moment. The only thing I knew for sure then was that I couldn't see anything in the mirror except the wallpaper behind me and the small table with the hairbrushes on it low against the wall.

I think I just stood there for perhaps ten seconds. Then I reached out and tried to touch the mirror, because I thought I was still asleep on the couch in the den and I figured that if I moved around a bit, so to speak, in my dream I could sort of jar myself awake. I know it isn't a very logical way to think, but in moments of stress we all do unusual things.

The first moment I really knew I was dead was when I couldn't feel the mirror. I couldn't even see the hand I had stretched out to touch it. That's when I knew there was nothing physical about me. I had identity, I was conscious, but I was invisible. I knew then I had to be either dead or a raving maniac.

Just to be sure, I stepped back into the den. I felt better when I saw my body lying on the couch. I guess that sounds like a peculiar thing to say, too, but what I mean is, I'd rather be dead than insane. Maybe *you* wouldn't but that's what makes horse races.

My next sensation (that's the only word I can think of to convey my meaning to you) was that there was something pressing on my mind, some nagging matter I had almost forgotten. It was very much like the feeling you sometimes have when you walk over to a bookshelf or a clothes closet, let's say, and then suddenly just stand there and say to yourself, "Now why did I come over here?" I felt a bit as if I had an imminent appointment.

I went over to the couch and looked down at myself. The magazine was open on the floor where it had slipped from my hand, and my right foot had fallen down as if I might have been making an effort to get up when I died.

It must have been the round of golf that did it. Larkin had warned me about exertion as long as three years ago, but after a fearful six months I had gotten steadily more overconfident. I was physically big, robust, muscular. I had played football at college. Inactivity annoyed the hell out of me. I remembered the headache that had plagued me over the last three holes, the feeling of utter weariness in the locker room after the game. But the cold shower had refreshed me a bit and a drink had relaxed me. I felt pretty good when I got home, except for an inner weariness and a lingering trace of the headache.

It had come while I was asleep, that's why I didn't recognize it. I mean if it comes in the form of a death-bed scene, with people standing around you shaking their heads, or if it comes in the form of a bullet from an angry gun, or in the form of drowning, well, it certainly comes as no surprise. But it came to me while I was lying there asleep in the den after reading a magazine. What with the sun and the exercise and the drink, I was a little groggy anyway and my dreams were sort of wild and confused. Naturally, when I found myself standing in front of the mirror I thought it was all just another part of a dream.

It wasn't, of course. You know that. You do if you read the papers, anyway, because they played it up pretty big on page one. "Westchester Man 'Dead' for 16 Minutes." That was the headline in the *Herald Tribune*. In the Chicago *Daily News* the headline on the story was "New Yorker 'Dead' Revived by Doctors." Notice those quotation marks around the word *dead*. That's always the way the papers handle it. I say always because it happens all the time. Last year alone there were nine of us around the country. Ask any of us about it and we'll just laugh good-naturedly and tell you the papers were right, we weren't dead. Of course we'll tell you that. What else could we tell you?

So there I was, beside the couch, staring down at myself. I remember looking around the room, but I was alone. They hadn't come yet. I felt a flicker of some kind that would be hard to describe—an urgency, an anxiety, a realization that I had left a few things undone. Then I tried a ridiculous thing. I tried to get back into myself. But it wouldn't work. I couldn't do it alone.

Jo would have to help, although we had just had a bitter argument. She had been in the kitchen when I had gone in to take a nap. I hurried to the kitchen. She was still there. Shelling peas, I think, and talking to the cook. "Jo," I said, but of course she couldn't hear me. I moved close to her and tried to tell her. I felt like a dog trying to interest a distracted master.

"Agnes," she said, "would you please close the window."

That's all she said. Then she stood up, wiped her hands, and walked out of the kitchen and down the hall to the den. I don't know how I did it, but in a vague way she had gotten the message.

She let out a tiny scream when she saw the color of my face. Then she shook me twice and then she said, "Oh, my God," and started to cry, quietly. She did not go to pieces. Thank God she didn't go to pieces or I wouldn't be able to tell the tale today.

Still crying, she ran to the hall phone and called Larkin. He ordered an ambulance and met it at the house inside of ten minutes. In all, only twelve minutes had elapsed since I had tried to look at myself in the mirror.

I remember Larkin came in on the run without talking. He ran past me as I stood at the door of the den and knelt down beside my body on the couch.

"When did you find him?" he said.

"Ten minutes ago," Jo said.

He took something out of his bag and injected the body with

adrenalin, and then they bundled "me" off to the hospital. I followed. It was five minutes away.

I never would have believed a crew could work so fast. Oxygen. More adrenalin. And then one of the doctors pushed a button and the table my body was on began to lift slowly, first at one end and then at the other, like a slow teeter-totter.

"Watch for blood pressure," Larkin whispered to an assistant, who squeezed a rubber bulb.

I was so fascinated watching them I did not at first realize I had visitors.

"Interesting," a voice said.

"Yes," I answered, without consciously directing my attention away from the body on the tilting table. Then I felt at one and the same time a pang of fear and the release of the nagging anxiety that had troubled me earlier.

I must have been expecting them. There was one on each side of me.

The second one looked at the body, then at Larkin and the others. "Do you think they'll succeed?" he said.

"I don't know," I said. "I hope so."

The answer seemed significant. The two looked at each other.

"We must be very certain," he said. "Would it matter so much to you either way?"

"Why, yes," I said. "I suppose it would. I mean, there's work I've left unfinished."

"Work isn't important *now*, is it?" asked the first one.

"No," I agreed. "It isn't. But there are other things. Things I have to do for Jo. For the children."

Again the two seemed to confer, silently.

"What sort of things?"

"Oh," I said, "there are some business details I've left up in the air. There'll be legal trouble, I'm sure, about the distribution of the assets of my firm."

"Is that all?" the first one said, coming closer to me. Larkin began to shake his head slowly. He looked as if he were losing hope.

Then I thought of something else. "You'll laugh," I said, "but something silly just came into my mind."

"What is it?" asked the second one.

"I would like to apologize to Jo," I said, "because we had an argument this afternoon. I'd forgotten I'd promised to take her and the children out to dinner and a movie. We had an argument about it. I suppose it sounds ridiculous at a time like this to talk about something that may seem so trivial, but that's what I'd like to do. I'd like to apologize to her for the things I said, and I'd like to keep that date. I'd like to take the children to see that movie, even if it is some cowboys-and-Indians thing that'll bore the hell out of me."

That's when it all began to happen. I can't say that suddenly the two were gone. To say *I* was gone would be more to the point. They didn't leave me. I left them. I was still unconscious, but now I was on the table. I was back inside my head. I was dreaming and I was dizzy. I didn't know what was happening in the room then, of course. I didn't know anything till later that night when I woke up. I felt weak and shaky and for a few minutes I wasn't aware that Larkin and some other doctors and Jo were standing around my bed. There was some kind of an oxygen tent over my chest and head, and my mouth felt dry and stiff. My tongue was like a piece of wood but I was alive. And I could see Jo. She looked tired and wan but she looked mighty beautiful to me.

The next day the men from the papers came around and interviewed me. They wrote that I was in good spirits and was sitting up in bed swapping jokes with the nurses, which was something of an exaggeration.

It was almost a month before I could keep that date with Jo and the kids, and by that time the picture wasn't even playing in our neighborhood. We had to drive all the way over to Claremont to see it, but we stopped at a nice tearoom on the way and had a wonderful dinner.

People still ask me what I felt while I was "dead." They always say it just that way, getting quotation marks into their voices, treating it as something a little bit amusing, the way the newspapers did. And I go along with it, of course. You can't say to them, "Why, yes, I was dead." They'd lock you up.

Funny thing about it all was that I'd always been more or less afraid of the idea of death. But after dying, I wasn't. I always knew I'd eventually go again, but it never worried me. I did my best to make a go of my relationships with other people and that was about the size of it. One other thing I did was write this little story and give it to a friend of mine, to be published only after my death.

If you're reading it, that means I've gone again. But this time I won't be back.

PHYLLIS McGINLEY

Ballade of Lost Objects

Where are the ribbons I tie my hair with?
    Where is my lipstick? Where are my hose —
The sheer ones hoarded these weeks to wear with
    Frocks the closets do not disclose?
Perfumes, petticoats, sports chapeaux,
    The blouse Parisian, the earring Spanish —
Everything suddenly ups and goes.
    And where in the world did the children vanish?

This is the house I used to share with
    Girls in pinafores, shier than does.
I can recall how they climbed my stair with
    Gales of giggles, on their tiptoes.
Last seen wearing both braids and bows
    (But looking rather Raggedy-Annish).
When they departed nobody knows —
    Where in the world did the children vanish?

Two tall strangers, now, I must bear with,
    Decked in my personal furbelows,
Raiding the larder, rending the air with
    Gossip and terrible radios.
Neither my friends nor quite my foes,
    Alien, beautiful, stern, and clannish,
Here they dwell, while the wonder grows:
    Where in the world did the children vanish?

Prince, I warn you, under the rose,
    Time is the thief you cannot banish,
These are my daughters, I suppose.
    But where in the world did the children vanish?

WILLIAM BROUCHNER

Out of Control

Main Characters

WALTER DAVIDSON. *A hard-hitting, courageous editorial writer, Walter is afraid of nothing — except perhaps the disapproval of his seventeen-year-old son. Walter loves the boy so much he has forgotten that firmness and authority are as much a part of paternal responsibility as solicitude and comfort.*

ELLIE DAVIDSON, *Walter's wife, has many of the same virtues and faults as her husband. She is attractive and intelligent. Although civic-minded, she is by no means the stereotyped clubwoman.*

CHIP DAVIDSON, *Walter's seventeen-year-old son. He is thoroughly charming when he's getting his own way, but hard as nails when he's crossed.*

CHARLIE LARSON, *Chip's pal. Charlie is just as spoiled as Chip, but lacks the latter's charm. He covers his inadequacies with an air of supercilious amusement.*

LIEUTENANT SANDERS, *a crisp and efficient police officer. He is blunt-spoken, but with a certain amount of tolerant amusement.*

(SCENE 1. FADE IN:[1] STOCK SHOT[2] — NIGHT — SMALL CITY. *A peaceful night shot of a small city. Over this is the narrator's voice.*)

1. *FADE IN.* The picture appears gradually from a blank screen.
2. *STOCK SHOT,* standard scene.

Narrator's voice: This story — a true one — happened at a place we'll call Watson Heights.

(SCENE 2. STOCK SHOT — NIGHT — A PARK. *It's at night and we see only an occasional passer-by.*)

Narrator's voice: An extremely pretty community, Watson Heights, known to the local Chamber of Commerce as the "City of Parks."

(SCENE 3. EXTERIOR PARK SET — NIGHT. *We're in a darkened section of the park and we see only the silhouettes of the participants in the next scene.*)

Narrator's voice: Population 32,784, most of them decent, honest people. Most of them.

(A man has paused at a public drinking fountain. We see his shadow straighten up, and then he is approached by a teen-ager.)

Teen-ager: Got a match, mister?

Man: Sure. *(hands him folder)* Might as well keep them, son. I've got plenty.

Teen-ager: Thanks, mister.

(Even now two other shadows are creeping up behind the man. He's slugged from behind and pummeled when he struggles. When he finally lies still, his attackers go through his pockets and we . . . DISSOLVE TO:[3]

(SCENE 4. INSERT — NEWSPAPER EDITORIAL. *All we have time to read is the title of the editorial:*

CRIME WAVE CONTINUES — MAN ATTACKED AND ROBBED IN PARK

(SCENE 5. INTERIOR DAVIDSON LIVING ROOM — CLOSE[4] — ELLIE DAVIDSON — LATER AFTERNOON. *Ellie is reading the newspaper editorial. Although her lips do not move, her background voice lets us know what the editorial is all about.*)

Ellie's voice: "Last night another of our citizens was robbed and beaten by teen-age hoodlums. This makes the third such vicious

3. *DISSOLVE TO.* The picture is fading out at the same time that another is fading in. Thus one picture blends into the next.
4. *CLOSE,* close-up, or close view (of Ellie Davidson).

crime since the trailer village opened last month and we can't help wondering if there isn't a connection. It's true that ——"

(Ellie's voice breaks off and she glances at the front door as her husband enters.)

Ellie: Hi, dear. *(As Ellie kisses him, Walter notes the newspaper in her hand.)*

Walter: Seen my editorial?

Ellie: I'm just now reading it. *(a slight frown)* Pretty strong words, don't you think?

Walter: Uh huh. And the one I'm writing for tomorrow's edition has even stronger words. *(grimly)* There's only one way to close down that trailer camp — and that's to hit hard and hit often.

Ellie: You're right, I suppose. *(The Davidsons' son, Chip, has emerged from the kitchen in time to hear Ellie's last speech. He's munching a sandwich.)*

Chip (effervescent): Of course he's right. My father is always right. My father is the smartest man in town — in the whole state — in the entire country — in the ———

Walter (interrupting good-naturedly): Okay, okay. What is it you want, Chip?

Chip: Howsabout the use of the car?

Walter (shakes his head regretfully): Not tonight, Chip. I have a committee meeting after dinner.

Chip: But, Dad, I promised the guys I'd provide transportation.

Walter: Sorry. *(Ellie sees the disappointment on her son's face. Then, to her husband . . .)*

Ellie: Couldn't you get a ride downtown with Roy Henry, Walter?

Walter: Chip's had the car every night this week, Ellie.

Ellie: I know, but . . . *(She trails off, eyeing the boy fondly. After a moment Walter sighs in good-natured resignation.)*

Walter: I don't know why I even bother to put up an argument. *(to Chip)* All right, you can have the car.

Chip (approvingly): That's my Pop. *(kisses mother)* I won't be home for dinner, Mom. *(starts to leave)*

Walter: Don't you want the car keys?

Chip (shakes head): I had a set of my own made yesterday.

(jingles keys) This way I won't have to borrow yours all the time.

Walter (dryly): Very considerate of you, I must say. *(Walter winks at his wife as Chip starts for the kitchen on his way to the back door of the house.)*

Ellie: Sometimes I think we let him have his own way too much.

*Walter: Some*times! *(They both chuckle.*

SCENE 6. EXTERIOR GARAGE . . . *as Chip emerges from the kitchen and hops into the car, which is in the driveway. The garage door is down. A moment later his father follows him out of the house.)*

Walter: Oh, Chip!

Chip: Yeah, Dad? (CAMERA MOVES IN CLOSER *as Walter walks to where his son is seated behind the wheel.)*

Walter: You've fallen way behind in your homework, so get back early tonight.

Chip: Sure, Dad.

Walter: And another thing, you'd better——

Chip (breaks in kiddingly): I'd better keep away from Memorial Park because that's where the naughty boys from the trailer camp seem to hang out.

Walter: It's no joking matter, Chip.

Chip (soothingly): I know, Dad. Now stop worrying your pretty head about me. *(Chip grins at his father and starts to back the car out of the driveway.*

(SCENE 7. CLOSE — WALTER . . . *watching his son drive off. He winces slightly as Chip, having backed out,* SQUEALS THE TIRES *in a turn and* ROARS OFF. *Then again Walter sighs helplessly and starts back for the house).* DISSOLVE TO:

(SCENE 8. INTERIOR DAVIDSON LIVING ROOM — NIGHT — CLOSE ON CLOCK. *It's twelve-thirty.* CAMERA DRAWS BACK *to include Walter and Ellie as the former throws another anxious glance at the clock.)*

Walter: Twelve-thirty. And I told him to be home early.

Ellie: Now, Walter, getting mad won't do any good.

Walter: I suppose not. *(sighs)* I wouldn't worry so much if those trailer toughs hadn't practically taken over the town.

Ellie (more troubled than she's letting on): But you've warned Chip time and again to keep away from the trouble zones.

Walter: Sure I have. But you know Chip. He always goes ahead and does exactly as he pleases. He—— *(Walter breaks off as Ellie holds up her hand, her head cocked to listen. We hear a car entering the driveway . . .* SOUND *. . . and they both "whew-w" with relief.*

(SCENE 9. EXTERIOR GARAGE *. . . as Chip halts the car, jumps out, and unlocks the garage door. He starts to pull up the garage door, but almost immediately there is a severe* EXPLOSION. *Chip is hurled back to the ground.*)

(SCENE 10. INTERIOR LIVING ROOM—CLOSE—WALTER AND ELLIE *. . . reacting to the explosion. After a moment of numbed, bewildered shock, Walter races for the garage, his wife in his wake.)*

(SCENE 11. EXTERIOR GARAGE—CLOSE—CHIP. *He sits up, shaking his head groggily.* CAMERA PULLS BACK *as his anxious parents reach him.*)

Walter: You all right, Chip?

Chip (dazed): I—I think so. *(Chip tests his arms and legs, then nods reassuringly at his parents.)*

Ellie: What happened?

Chip (bewildered): I don't know. I was opening up the garage when all of a sudden, *whammo! (Walter has moved closer to the garage door to inspect the damage.)*

Ellie: Careful, Walter. It might happen again.

Walter: No. Bombs go off only once. *(Walter is examining the door, hardly able to believe his eyes. His wife and son glance at him incredulously.)*

Ellie: Bombs?

Walter: Somebody rigged one to the garage door. *(They stare at each other. It's just too fantastic to be true and yet it is true. Then Walter moves toward the house.)*

Walter (continuing): I'm going to call the police.
(DISSOLVE TO:

SCENE 12. EXTERIOR GARAGE—NIGHT—CLOSE ON BOMB FRAGMENTS . . . *as police officer's hands pick up the fragments carefully.* CAMERA DRAWS BACK *as the officer, McCabe, carries the fragments over to Lieutenant Sanders, who seems to be in charge of the investigation. Walter hovers nearby.)*

McCabe: It was a bomb, all right, Lieutenant. *(indicates fragments)* A homemade job.

Lieutenant (glances from the fragments to Walter): Seems as if somebody's real mad at you, Mr. Davidson . . . Any idea who? *(at Walter's slow nod)* Oh?

Walter: I work for the *Evening Tribune* and I've written a series of editorials blasting the trailer village. *(looks at fragments)* It wouldn't surprise me a bit if this were a return blast.

Lieutenant: It would me. *(to officer)* Have the lab check all fragments, McCabe. *(McCabe nods and moves off. Walter, puzzled, has been looking at the Lieutenant questioningly.)*

Lieutenant (continuing): I've been reading your editorials, Mr. Davidson. You seem sold on the idea that trailer camps breed delinquency.

Walter: Lots of other people feel the same way.

Lieutenant: Uh huh. And *they're* wrong, too. *(grins)* I live in a trailer, Mr. Davidson.

Walter: Then there's the possibility you might be prejudiced.

Lieutenant: Sure. But I doubt if national police figures are prejudiced and according to them the delinquency rate in trailer camps is way below the average. Living in such close quarters the kids are pretty much under supervision all the time, and as a rule they don't get into trouble. They——

McCabe: Lieutenant. Can you come here a minute? *(Officer McCabe has been examining a broken window on the side of the garage. The lieutenant walks over to him, Walter following.*

SCENE 13. CLOSER SHOT—WALTER, LIEUTENANT, AND MCCABE. *McCabe has a burlap sack in his hand.)*

McCabe: They went through the window to plant the bomb inside. The noise of breaking glass was muffled with this. *(indicates the sack)*

Lieutenant: The Blue Moons again, you think?

McCabe (shrugs): That's their usual technique. *(The lieutenant nods thoughtfully, but the name "Blue Moons" hasn't meant a thing to Walter.)*

Walter: The Blue Moons? Who're the Blue Moons?

Lieutenant: A juvenile gang that's been giving the police a bad time. The way things are going, we need a much bigger force.

Walter (almost triumphant): And yet you say the trailer village hasn't attracted an undesirable element?

Lieutenant (patiently): The Blue Moons have been operating for quite a while, Mr. Davidson—long before the first trailer arrived.

Walter: But what have they got against *me?* I didn't even know such a gang existed.

Lieutenant: Maybe you're not the one they were after.

Walter: I don't understand.

Lieutenant: Where'd your boy go?

Walter (frowns, beginning to understand the drift of the policeman's thoughts): In the house. His mother's fixing him some hot chocolate. *(They start for the house together.*

SCENE 14. INTERIOR LIVING ROOM—FULL.[5] *Ellie is placing hot chocolate and cookies on an end table beside Chip's chair.)*

Ellie: If it's hot just let it set awhile.

Chip: Thanks, Mom. *(They both glance up as Walter and the lieutenant enter.)*

Walter: The lieutenant has a few questions to ask you, Chip. *(Chip's manner is unfrightened and straightforward as he nods at the police officer.)*

Chip: Sure. Go right ahead.

Lieutenant: How come you were out past the curfew tonight, Chip?

Chip: Golly, Lieutenant, nobody pays any attention to that curfew

---

5. *FULL.* The camera shows as much of the living room as possible.

law. *(The lieutenant glances at Walter who reacts defensively.)*

Walter: He tells me he went to the drive-in movie with some friends and they stayed late to see the show a second time. I don't see anything so terrible about that. *(The lieutenant shrugs, not committing himself one way or the other. Then he again turns to Chip.)*

Lieutenant: What do you know about the Blue Moon gang, son?

Chip: Not much. You hear things around school, of course, but never anything definite. I guess it's supposed to be a kind of secret organization.

Lieutenant: You're not a member, then? *(at Chip's headshake)* How about the Dragons? Ever hear of them? *(Chip sipping his hot chocolate, reacts ever so slightly. When he speaks, his tone is a little too casual.)*

Chip: The Dragons? That's a new one on me.

Lieutenant (studying him): They started up only recently. I understand the members carry a little Dragon emblem on their car keys.

Chip: Is that so?

Lieutenant: Mind letting me have a look at your car keys, Chip?

Chip (rattled): I don't have any. . . . I—I use Dad's all the time.

(His parents know this for a lie, but are too shocked to speak.)

Lieutenant (quietly): I see.

Walter: Have you any reason to believe the Dragons have been causing trouble?

Lieutenant (shakes head): So far, all the Juvenile Officer has been able to find out is that the organization exists.

Walter: Well, then?

Lieutenant: Earlier tonight two of the Blue Moon gang were beaten up. Badly beaten up. Brass knuckles. They refused to tell us who did it—said they'd take care of the matter themselves. (CAMERA FOLLOWS *Walter and the lieutenant as they move away from Ellie and Chip toward the door at the other end of the room.*)

Walter (slowly): And you're wondering if the bomb wasn't their way of taking care of it?

Lieutenant: Let me put it this way, Mr. Davidson—for your sake I hope Chip is telling the truth.

Walter: For *my* sake?

Lieutenant (nods): Because if he's lying—and he can do it *that* convincingly—you've got a *real* problem on your hands. *(The policeman goes out the door. His tone has been only half-kidding, and Walter's face is grim as he returns to his son.* CAMERA MOVES CLOSER *as Walter holds out his hand for the keys. Chip hesitates, then fishes the keys out of his pocket. Ellie stares in appalled silence as Walter holds up the little Dragon emblem. Chip looks up with an incredulous expression on his face.)*

Chip: You think *I* brass-knuckled somebody? *(He receives no answer and goes on, fervently.)* Dad, I give you my word of honor that the Dragons don't go in for that hard-guy stuff. I don't think any of us would recognize brass knuckles if we saw them.

Walter: Suppose you tell me what you *do* know about the Dragons, Chip.

Chip: We're not a *gang* like the Blue Moons, Dad. Honest. *(Looks earnestly at his parents)* The Dragons are a social club.

Walter: Then why didn't you tell your mother and me that you'd joined?

Chip: Because when I was initiated I had to swear to keep my membership secret. It's a rule of the club.

(SCENE 15. CLOSE—WALTER AND CHIP. *Walter is slightly relieved at the explanation, although he gives his son a troubled, questioning look. As Chip smiles at his father reassuringly, we . . .* DISSOLVE TO:

SCENE 16. EXTERIOR GARAGE—NIGHT. *Chip has gone to bed and Walter comes out to check the car. He removes Chip's folded raincoat from the seat, starts to bring it in when something metallic falls on the pavement.)*

Narrator's voice: All at once nothing would ever be quite the same again. In the excitement following the bomb explosion Chip had forgotten to remove something from its temporary hiding place. (CAMERA MOVES IN CLOSE *on a pair of brass knuckles as Walter picks them up. Over this we hear the lieutenant's voice.*)

Lieutenant's voice: Because if he's lying—and he can do it *that* convincingly—you've got a *real* problem on your hands.

(FADE OUT)[6]

(SCENE 17. FADE IN: INTERIOR DAVIDSON LIVING ROOM—DAY—CLOSE ON BRASS KNUCKLES. *Ellie is holding the brass knuckles in her hand.*)

Narrator's voice: What do you do when you find out something like this about your own son? When you come upon a part of him you never even suspected. (CAMERA HAS BEEN PULLING BACK, *and we see that Ellie is staring disbelievingly at the brass knuckles she holds. Walter is talking on the phone.*)

Narrator's voice: At first you refuse to accept it. *(Ellie shakes her head as if denying the existence of the knuckles. She puts them down with loathing and turns to her husband.*

SCENE 18. CLOSE—WALTER . . . *talking into phone.)*

Walter: Yes. Yes, I see. Well, thank you very much. *(As he hangs up.* CAMERA PULLS BACK *to include Ellie.)*

Walter: Chip hasn't showed up at school yet.

Ellie: But it's after nine. *(a frightening thought)* Do you suppose he's been in an accident, Walter? That Larson boy came by and picked Chip up in his car. The way he drives. . . . *(She trails off as Walter shakes his head wearily.)*

Walter: The school tells me Chip missed all his classes yesterday, too. Apparently it's been happening at least a couple of days every week.

Ellie (shocked): And the school lets them get away with it? *(indignant)* No wonder the youngsters in this town are getting out of control.

Walter (again shakes his head): The school had no way of know-

6. *FADE OUT*. The picture fades, or disappears gradually, until the screen is blank.

ing anything was wrong. Chip turns in a signed excuse after every absence.

Ellie (bewildered): Signed? By whom?

Walter: By me. Or rather with my name. . . . Forged, of course. *(Ellie sits down despairingly. She can no longer deny to herself that something is radically wrong with her son and she's on the verge of tears.)*

Ellie: What's happened to the boy, Walter? *(desperately)* What's making him do these things? What. . . . *(She can't go on. Walter goes to her comfortingly.)*

Walter: We'll get it straightened out, honey, don't you worry.

Ellie: But overnight he's changed from a decent youngster into a . . . *(groping)* into the kind of a boy who could use those horrible things. *(Her glance has gone to the brass knuckles. Walter picks them up.)*

Walter: I think it's more than just overnight, Ellie. I think it's probably been coming on for quite a while—ever since he started traveling around with the Larson boy and that crowd.

Ellie (helpless): But what'll we *do?*

Walter: Is Charlie Larson apt to show up here again today?

Ellie (nods): He usually drops Chip off at the house about three-thirty — just as if they'd been together at school all day.

Walter (nods as if having come to a decision): I've got to get down to the paper now, but I'll knock off early. I'll be home before three-thirty.

Ellie: What do you have in mind, Walter?

Walter (tight-lipped anger): When young Mr. Larson gets here, he's going to get the dressing-down of his life. *(And as Walter thrusts the brass knuckles into his pocket, we . . .* DISSOLVE TO:

SCENE 19. EXTERIOR GARAGE — DAY . . . *as Charlie Larson halts his battered heap in the driveway. Chip, hopping out of the car, is surprised to see his father emerge from the house.)*

Chip: Hi, Dad. What are you doing home so early?

Walter: Something came up. . . . I'd like to have a talk with you and your friend Charlie if you've got a minute. *(The boys sense that something is in the wind. They're not frightened by any means, but they exchange a quizzical glance.)*

Chip: Okay, Charlie?

Charlie: Why not?

(SCENE 20. INTERIOR LIVING ROOM — FULL — *Ellie has been watching nervously out the window, but she comes away from it as Walter, Chip, and Charlie enter the house. Ad lib hellos; then . . .*)

Walter: Have a seat, Chip. You too, Charlie.

Charlie: Thanks. *(There's the faintest touch of amusement in Charlie's tone, as if he knows what's coming and doesn't care. Walter has drawn Ellie to one side.)*

Walter (low): I think it'd be better if you waited in the kitchen, Ellie.

Ellie: All right, but — try to take it easy, Walt. *(He nods and Ellie goes out. Walter moves closer to the boys.*

SCENE 21. ANOTHER ANGLE.)

Walter (eyes Charlie speculatively): How was school today, Charlie?

Charlie: Same as always. Dull.

Walter: Charlie, it's my guess you never went anywhere near the school today.

Charlie (a small smile): That's a pretty good guess, Mr. Davidson. *(He shrugs indifferently turning to Chip.)* What's with this Dick Tracy bit anyway?

Chip: Charlie's a friend of mine, Dad. You can't treat him like that.

Walter (bitterly): A fine friend!

Charlie (emits a sigh of long suffering): So Chip and I had a few laughs at the lake instead of sleeping through classes. What's so terrible?

Walter: And forging excuses? That's perfectly harmless, too, I suppose. And these. . . . *(takes out brass knuckles)* From your point of view these don't mean a thing, do they, Charlie?

Charlie (eyes the knuckles narrowly): Where'd you get them?

Walter: My son forgot and left them in the car last night.

Charlie (tsk-tsks at Chip in mock disapproval, then turns back to Walter): Let me get something straight, Mr. Davidson. You figure I'm a bad influence on Chip, is that it?

Walter: You and the rest of the Dragon gang, yes. *(at Charlie's chuckle)* And I don't consider it particularly funny.

Charlie: That's because you've never heard my old man on the same subject. According to him, Chip is a bad influence on *me.* *(Walter throws a startled glance at his son who has been listening imperturbably.)*

Walter: That's absurd.

Chip (easily): Sure it is. And it's just as absurd to think that Charlie influences me. Nobody tells either of us what to do. Nobody.

Walter (firmly): Just the same, you're resigning from that gang as of right now.

Chip: Nobody, Dad. *(Chip meets his father's stern glance without flinching.)*

Walter: Are you defying me, Chip? *(Chip's hands go up in a gesture of impatience.)*

Chip: What's got into you all at once, Dad? Ever since I got home you've been making noises like one of those old-fashioned, razor-strop fathers.

Walter: Chip, I'm ordering you to resign.

Chip: Ordering me, Dad? Like I was a trained poodle or something?

Walter: No. Like you were my son.

Chip: Either way it doesn't set well. I guess I just don't much care for orders. Come on, Charlie. *(Charlie nods and follows Chip toward the door.)*

Walter (sternly): Come back here, Chip!

Chip (turns, but his face is stony and his tone flat): Tell Mom I won't be home for dinner. *(goes out the door)*

Charlie (waves an airy, sardonic good-bye): So long, Mr. Davidson.

(SCENE 22. CLOSE — WALTER. *He sits down heavily, helplessly.*

We hear the ROAR *of Charlie's car as the boys leave. When Ellie appears from the kitchen, she too is extremely distressed.)*

Walter: Did you hear everything? *(at Ellie's nod)* As if I were some kind of hired hand around here. That's the way he talked to me. My own son.

Ellie: He wouldn't have been so rude if that Larson boy hadn't been egging him on.

Walter: Yes, he would have, Ellie. It's no use looking for somebody else to blame. I've already been all through that. *(sighs tiredly)* I tried to pin it on bad company, on the school system, even — so help me — on the trailer park. I've pointed the finger everywhere but where it belongs. *(points to himself)* Right here.

Ellie: But you've done everything in the world for Chip.

Walter: I spoiled him rotten if that's what you mean. I let him have his own way because it was easier to be liked than respected.

Ellie: I'm as much at fault as you are. Lots of times you'd say "no" and then I'd talk you into changing your mind. *(Walter realizes his wife is trying to lighten the burden, and he gets up to kiss her gratefully.)*

Walter: Thanks, Ellie. But I'm supposed to be head of the household, and it was up to me to make a "no" stick. *(Walter is moving to the telephone. As he dials . . .)* You can't expect a youngster to have respect for the police or any other kind of authority if he's never run up against authority in his own home. They——*(into mouthpiece)* Hello. This is Davidson. Let me speak to Schilling, please. *(to Ellie)* Would you get my portable typewriter out of the hall closet, El? *(She nods and moves off.*

SCENE 23. CLOSE — WALTER.)

Walter (into mouthpiece): Jim? Davidson here. You know that editorial I wrote for today? Well, tear it up. Yes, tear it up. Don't worry, I'll have another piece for you before your deadline. . . . Yeah, promise. . . . Bye, Jim. (CAMERA PULLS BACK *as he hangs up and goes to table where Ellie has placed his typewriter. He struggles for a moment to remove the portable's cover.)*

Walter: Blast this cover. It always sticks.

Ellie: Now, Walter, getting mad won't do any good.

Walter: I think maybe you're wrong, Ellie. *(wrenches cover free)* I think maybe getting mad is exactly what the fathers in this town need. *(Walter sits down and begins to type.*

SCENE 24. INSERT — TYPEWRITER . . . *as Walter taps out the title of his editorial:*

OLD-FASHIONED — A DIRTY WORD?

SCENE 25. CLOSE — WALTER. *As he types, his voice tells us what he is writing.)*

Walter's voice: My father was an old-fashioned man. It was his conviction that youngsters need rules and discipline as much as they need food and air, and so *he* formulated the rules and *he* disciplined those of his children who broke them. We kids all knew exactly where we stood at all times and we were happy.

(DISSOLVING TO:

SCENE 26. INSERT — NEWSPAPER EDITORIAL. *This is Walter's editorial as printed. Walter's voice has faded off and is replaced by the voice of Charlie, who is reading it out loud.*)

Charlie's voice: Nowadays too many fathers are leaving rules and discipline to the schools, to the police, to their wives, and the result is a new type of juvenile delinquent — the overprivileged delinquent who knows no law but his own whim.

(SCENE 27. EXTERIOR PARK SET — NIGHT — CHIP, CHARLIE, JUNIOR, AND BERT. *Junior and Bert are perhaps a year younger than Chip and Charlie, but pretty much the same type. All four of them are lounging around a park bench while Charlie reads the editorial with the aid of an overhead light.*)

Charlie: He steals, not because he needs money, but "for kicks." He joins a gang and fights other gangs, not out of anger, but "for kicks." He is spoiled, confused, and miserable——*(stops reading to address Chip ironically)* You hear that, Chip? Your father writes you're spoiled, confused, and miserable.

Chip (indifferently): Yeah.

Charlie (reading again): . . . and he'll only get more spoiled, more confused, more miserable unless dear old Dad reinstates himself as head of the household. And so on and so on and so on. *(tosses paper aside)* What a laugh. *(Bert and Junior appear a little worried.)*

Bert: I dunno about that. After my old man read it, he told me to be in early tonight or else.

Junior: Mine got all excited, too. *(to Chip)* He got busy on the phone and there's going to be some kind of fathers' meeting at your house.

Charlie: It don't mean a thing, Junior. Like they're always saying about us — it's just a phase they're passing through.

Junior (not convinced): What'd your old man have to say about it?

Charlie: He's out of town.

Junior (jeering): No wonder you're talking so big. *(To this Charlie has no reply, but Chip steps into the breach. Chip's tone is harsh.)*

Chip: My father's not out of town. Do you see me running for cover?

Junior (immediately goes on the defensive): I'm not going to be bluffed either. Chip—you know that. Me and Bert have a couple of chicks dated at the other end of the park, and we'll get home when we feel like it. Right, Bert?

Bert (firmly): Right. *(less firmly)* Just the same, though, I'd like to know what's going on at that meeting.

(DISSOLVE TO:

SCENE 28. INTERIOR DAVIDSON LIVING ROOM — NIGHT — FULL SHOT. *There are several fathers crowded into the living room. Dale Armstrong is speaking.)*

Armstrong: It seems to me that you feel the main trouble with this generation is that they haven't been beaten often enough. Am I right?

Walter (chuckles but shakes his head): No, Dale. Our kids have been running wild, and it's up to us to bring them back under control — but personally I don't think that discipline necessarily means physical punishment.

Armstrong: I don't see how it can be done without cracking a few heads together.

Walter: Let's hope it doesn't come to that.

Armstrong: But if it *does?*

Walter (sighs, then reluctantly): In that case I guess we'll just have to crack a few heads together. *(consults watch)* Gentlemen, it's almost ten. We don't have much time to make up our minds.

(There's a hum of pros and cons as we . . . DISSOLVE TO:

SCENE 29. EXTERIOR CITY STREET — NIGHT — CAR. *A car with four or five men in it is slowly cruising the street.)*

Narrator's voice: A decision was reached and the fathers at the meeting immediately got in touch with other fathers. That night they patrolled the town — in cars . . .

(QUICK DISSOLVE TO:

SCENE 30. EXTERIOR PARK SET—NIGHT. *We're in the same darkened section of the park we saw very early in the story, and once again the scene can be done in silhouette. A patrolling father approaches the drinking fountain.)*

Narrator's voice (continuing): . . . and on foot. *(As the father pauses at the fountain, he is approached by a teen-ager.)*

Teen-ager: Got a match, mister? *(The father pulls out a whistle and blows it. In a matter of seconds, the startled teen-ager is surrounded by other fathers seemingly coming from nowhere.*

QUICK DISSOLVE TO:

SCENE 31. EXTERIOR PARKED CAR — FULL SHOT — NIGHT. *We see Bert and Junior, each with a girl, in the car. All four youngsters are startled and scared as paternal hands haul them out of the parked vehicle.)*

Narrator's voice: Youngsters found on the streets were given the choice of going home immediately or of being turned over to the police for violation of the ten o'clock curfew. In all instances it was made clear that the fathers were acting not as policemen but as parents.

(QUICK DISSOLVE TO:

SCENE 32. EXTERIOR PARK — NIGHT — CHIP AND CHARLIE. *The two boys are pitching pennies in the same part of the park where we saw them last. Charlie looks around puzzledly.)*

Charlie: Where is everybody tonight, you suppose?

Chip (shrugs): Search me. *(He goes to retrieve the pennies.*

SCENE 33. CLOSE — CHIP . . . *as he bends down to pick up coins. Walter's legs come into the scene.* CAMERA DRAWS BACK *as Chip looks up at his father. Charlie approaches interestedly. Neither boy demonstrates the slightest fear.)*

Walter: Time you were home, isn't it, Chip?

Chip: Ten-thirty. Who goes home at ten-thirty?

Walter (evenly): You do. Ten o'clock's the legal curfew and from now on you'll obey the law. *(Father and son eye each other steadily, neither's glance wavering. Then . . .)*

Chip: You really think you're big enough to make me, Dad?

Walter (opens his hand, revealing a whistle): All I have to do is blow this whistle and there'll be ten other fathers here in no time.

Charlie (chuckles softly): What happens when you don't have your whistle with you, Mr. Davidson? How do you make Chip obey then?

Walter (his eyes on Chip): Good question, Charlie. And I guess I better find out the answer right now. *(He tosses the whistle into the bushes.)* Come on home, Chip.

Chip: Why should I?

Walter: Because I'm your father and I'm telling you to.

Charlie: Don't do it, Chip. *(regards Walter with amusement)* Look at him. He's turning green.

Walter: If I am, Charlie, it's not because I'm afraid. It's because the idea of fighting with my own son makes me a little sick to the stomach.

Charlie: He's breaking my heart, Chip. Let's get away from here.

(Charlie puts his hand on Chip's arm, but Walter brushes it aside. All the while his glance is still locked with Chip's.)

Walter: Chip isn't going anywhere but straight home — not unless he steps over me.

Chip: All right, then. I'll step over you. *(Chip swings, catching his father flush on the jaw. Walter goes down. He shakes his head to clear it. Then . . .)*

Walter: This isn't going to prove a thing, Chip.

Chip: That mean you're quitting? *(By way of reply, Walter gets to his feet and starts to fight in earnest.)*

(SCENE 34. CLOSE — CHARLIE . . . *watching the fight with amusement. Without hurrying in the slightest, Charlie reaches into his pocket and pulls out a set of brass knuckles. There's an anticipatory smile on his face as he puts them on.*)

(SCENE 35. ANOTHER ANGLE — FEATURING[7] WALTER AND CHIP. *They're still fighting, and now Chip is getting the worst of it. Walter knocks Chip down and stands over him, panting heavily. At this point Charlie approaches meaningfully.*)

(SCENE 36. CLOSE. *Struggling to his feet, Chip sees what Charlie is up to. For a moment he remains frozen — almost hypnotized — then the spell breaks and he rushes toward Charlie.*)

(SCENE 37. WIDER ANGLE[8] . . . *as Chip swarms all over the astounded Charlie. A small smile of thankfulness appears on Walter's lips. Chip wrenches the brass knuckles off Charlie's hand and throws them into the bushes. Charlie replies with a blow.*)

Walter: That's enough of that, understand? *(Chip slowly lowers his fists.)*

Walter: Now let's get you boys home. *(He turns and walks away. Chip follows. Walter calls over his shoulder.)*

Walter: You, too, Charlie. *(Charlie stands undecided.)*

Narrator's voice: This was not the end but the beginning, and it would take many months before the gangs of Watson Heights were completely disbanded. (FADE OUT)

---

7. *FEATURING,* focusing attention on.
8. *WIDER ANGLE,* wider view of the scene.

CARSON McCULLERS

Sucker

It was always like I had a room to myself. Sucker slept in my bed with me but that didn't interfere with anything. The room was mine and I used it as I wanted to. Once I remember sawing a trap door in the floor. Last year when I was a sophomore in high school I tacked on my wall some pictures of girls from magazines and one of them was just in her underwear. My mother never bothered me because she had the younger kids to look after. And Sucker thought anything I did was always swell.

Whenever I would bring any of my friends back to my room all I had to do was just glance once at Sucker and he would get up from whatever he was busy with and maybe half smile at me, and leave without saying a word. He never brought kids back there. He's twelve, four years younger than I am, and he always knew without me even telling him that I didn't want kids that age meddling with my things.

Half the time I used to forget that Sucker isn't my brother. He's my first cousin but practically ever since I remember he's been in our family. You see, his folks were killed in a wreck when he was a baby. To me and my kid sisters he was like our brother.

Sucker used to always remember and believe every word I said. That's how he got his nickname. Once a couple of years ago I

---

told him that if he'd jump off our garage with an umbrella it would act as a parachute and he wouldn't fall hard. He did it and busted his knee. That's just one instance. And the funny thing was that no matter how many times he got fooled he would still believe me. Not that he was dumb in other ways — it was just the way he acted with me. He would look at everything I did and quietly take it in.

There is one thing I have learned, but it makes me feel guilty and hard to figure out. If a person admires you a lot you despise him and don't care — and it is the person who doesn't notice you that you are apt to admire. This is not easy to realize. Maybelle Watts, this senior at school, acted like she was the Queen of Sheba and even humiliated me. Yet at this same time I would have done anything in the world to get her attentions. All I could think about day and night was Maybelle until I was nearly crazy. When Sucker was a little kid and on up until the time he was twelve I guess I treated him as bad as Maybelle did me.

Now that Sucker has changed so much it is a little hard to remember him as he used to be. I never imagined anything would suddenly happen that would make us both very different. I never knew that in order to get what has happened straight in my mind I would want to think back on him as he used to be and compare and try to get things settled. If I could have seen ahead maybe I would have acted different.

I never noticed him much or thought about him and when you consider how long we have had the same room together it is funny the few things I remember. He used to talk to himself a lot when he'd think he was alone — all about him fighting gangsters and being on ranches and that sort of kids' stuff. He'd get in the bathroom and stay as long as an hour and sometimes his voice would go up high and excited and you could hear him all over the house. Usually, though, he was very quiet. He didn't have many boys in the neighborhood to buddy with and his face had the look of a kid who is watching a game and waiting to be asked to play. He didn't mind wearing the sweaters and coats that I outgrew, even if the sleeves did flop down too big and make his wrists look as thin and white as a little girl's. That is how I remember him — getting a little bigger every year but still being the same. That was Sucker up until a few months ago when all this trouble began.

Maybelle was somehow mixed up in what happened so I guess I ought to start with her. Until I knew her I hadn't given much time to girls. Last fall she sat next to me in General Science class and that was when I first began to notice her. Her hair is the brightest yellow I ever saw and occasionally she will wear it set into curls with some sort of gluey stuff. Her fingernails are pointed and manicured and painted a shiny red. All during class I used to watch Maybelle, nearly all the time except when I thought she was going to look my way or when the teacher called on me. I couldn't keep my eyes off her hands, for one thing. They are very little and white except for that red stuff, and when she would turn the pages of her book she always licked her thumb and held out her little finger and turned very slowly. It is impossible to describe Maybelle. All the boys are crazy about her but she didn't even notice me. All I could do was sit and look at her in class — and sometimes it was like the whole room could hear my heart beating and I wanted to holler or light out and run for hell.

At night, in bed, I would imagine about Maybelle. Often this would keep me from sleeping until as late as one or two o'clock. Sometimes Sucker would wake up and ask me why I couldn't get settled and I'd tell him hush his mouth. I suppose I was mean to him lots of times. I guess I wanted to ignore somebody like Maybelle did me. You could always tell by Sucker's face when his feelings were hurt. I don't remember all the ugly remarks I must have made because even when I was saying them my mind was on Maybelle.

That went on for nearly three months and then somehow she began to change. In the halls she would speak to me and every morning she copied my homework. At lunch time once I danced with her in the gym. One afternoon I got up nerve and went around to her house with a carton of cigarettes. I knew she smoked in the girls' basement and sometimes outside of school—and I didn't want to take her candy because I think that's been run into the ground. She was very nice and it seemed to me everything was going to change.

It was that night when this trouble really started. I had come into my room late and Sucker was already asleep. I felt too happy and keyed up to get in a comfortable position and I was awake thinking about Maybelle a long time. Then I dreamed about her and it seemed I kissed her. It was a surprise to wake up and see the dark. I lay still and a little while passed before I could come to and understand where I was. The house was quiet and it was a very dark night.

Sucker's voice was a shock to me. "Pete? . . ."

I didn't answer anything or even move.

"You do like me as much as if I was your own brother, don't you, Pete?"

I couldn't get over the surprise of everything and it was like this was the real dream instead of the other.

"You have liked me all the time like I was your own brother, haven't you?"

"Sure," I said.

Then I got up for a few minutes. It was cold and I was glad to come back to bed. Sucker hung on to my back. He felt little and warm and I could feel his warm breathing on my shoulder.

"No matter what you did I always knew you liked me."

I was wide awake and my mind seemed mixed up in a strange way. There was this happiness about Maybelle and all that — but at the same time something about Sucker and his voice when he said these things made me take notice. Anyway I guess you understand people better when you are happy than when something is worrying you. It was like I had never really thought about Sucker until then. I felt I had always been mean to him. One night a few weeks before I had heard him crying in the dark. He said he had lost a boy's beebee gun and was scared to let anybody know. He wanted me to tell him what to do. I was sleepy and tried to make him hush and when he wouldn't I kicked at him. That was just one of the things I remembered. It seemed to me he had always been a lonesome kid. I felt bad.

There is something about a dark cold night that makes you feel close to someone you're sleeping with. When you talk together it is like you are the only people awake in the town.

"You're a swell kid, Sucker," I said.

It seemed to me suddenly that I did like him more than anybody else I knew — more than any other boy, more than my sisters, more in a certain way even than Maybelle. I felt good all over and it was like when they play sad music in the movies. I wanted to show Sucker how much I really thought of him and make up for the way I had always treated him.

We talked for a good while that night. His voice was fast and it was like he had been saving up these things to tell me for a long time. He mentioned that he was going to try to build a canoe and that the kids down the block wouldn't let him in on their football team and I don't know what all. I talked some too and it was a good feeling to think of him taking in everything I said so seriously. I even spoke of Maybelle a little, only I made out like it was her who had been running after me all this time. He asked questions about high school and so forth. His voice was excited and he kept on talking fast like he could never get the words out in time. When I went to sleep he was still talking and I could still feel his breathing on my shoulder, warm and close.

During the next couple of weeks I saw a lot of Maybelle. She acted as though she really cared for me a little. Half the time I felt so good I hardly knew what to do with myself.

But I didn't forget about Sucker. There were a lot of old things in my bureau drawer I'd been saving — boxing gloves and Tom Swift books and second-rate fishing tackle. All this I turned over to him. We had some more talks together and it was really like I was knowing him for the first time. When there was a long cut on his cheek I knew he had been monkeying around with this new first razor set of mine, but I didn't say anything. His face seemed different now. He used to look timid and sort of like he was afraid of a whack over the head. That expression was gone. His face, with those wide-open eyes and his ears sticking out and his mouth never quite shut, had the look of a person who is surprised and expecting something swell.

Once I started to point him out to Maybelle and tell her he was my kid brother. It was an afternoon when a murder mystery was on at the movie. I had earned a dollar working for my Dad and I gave Sucker a quarter to go and get candy and so forth. With the rest I took Maybelle. We were sitting near the back and I saw Sucker come in. He began to stare at the screen the minute he stepped past the ticket man and he stumbled down the aisle without noticing where he was going. I started to punch Maybelle but couldn't quite make up my mind. Sucker looked a little silly — walking like a drunk with his eyes glued to the movie. He was wiping his reading glasses on his shirttail and his knickers flopped down. He went on until he got to the first few rows where the kids usually sit. I never did punch Maybelle. But I got to thinking it was good to have both of them at the movie with the money I earned.

I guess things went on like this for about a month or six weeks. I felt so good I couldn't settle down to study or put my mind on anything. I wanted to be friendly with everybody. There were times when I just had to talk to some person. And usually that would be Sucker. He felt as good as I did. Once he said: "Pete, I am gladder that you are like my brother than anything else in the world."

Then something happened between Maybelle and me. I never have figured out just what it was. Girls like her are hard to understand. She began to act different toward me. At first I wouldn't let myself believe this and tried to think it was just my imagination. She didn't act glad to see me any more. Often she went out riding with this fellow on the football team who owns this yellow roadster. The car was the color of her hair and after school she would ride off with him, laughing and looking into his face. I couldn't think of anything to do about it and she was on my mind all day and night. When I did get a chance to go out with her she was snippy and didn't seem to notice me. This made me feel like something was the matter — I would worry about my shoes clopping too loud on the floor, or the fly of my pants, or the bumps on my chin. Sometimes when Maybelle was around, a devil would get into me and I'd hold my face stiff and call grown men by their last names without the Mister and say rough things. In the night I would wonder what made me do all this until I was too tired for sleep.

At first I was so worried I just forgot about Sucker. Then later he began to get on my nerves. He was always hanging around until I would get back from high school, always looking like he had something to say to me or wanted me to tell him. He made me a magazine rack in his Manual Training class and one week he saved his lunch money and bought me three packs of cigarettes. He couldn't seem to take it in that I had things on my mind and didn't want to fool with him. Every afternoon it would be the same — him in my room with this waiting expression on his face. Then I wouldn't say anything or I'd maybe answer him rough-like and he would finally go on out.

I can't divide that time up and say this happened one day and that the next. For one thing I was so mixed up the weeks just slid along into each other and I felt like hell and didn't care. Nothing definite was said or done. Maybelle still rode around with this fellow in his yellow roadster and sometimes she would smile at me and sometimes not. Every afternoon I went from one place to another where I thought she would be. Either she would act almost nice and I would begin thinking how things would finally clear up and she would care for me — or else she'd behave so that if she hadn't been a girl I'd have wanted to grab her by that white little neck and choke her. The more ashamed I felt for making a fool of myself the more I ran after her.

Sucker kept getting on my nerves more and more. He would look at me as though he sort of blamed me for something, but at the same time knew that it wouldn't last long. He was growing fast and for some reason began to stutter when he talked. Sometimes he had nightmares or would throw up his breakfast. Mom got him a bottle of cod liver oil.

Then the finish came between Maybelle and me. I met her

going to the drugstore and asked for a date. When she said no I remarked something sarcastic. She told me she was sick and tired of my being around and that she had never cared a rap about me. She said all that. I just stood there and didn't answer anything. I walked home very slowly.

For several afternoons I stayed in my room by myself. I didn't want to go anywhere or talk to anyone. When Sucker would come in and look at me sort of funny I'd yell at him to get out. I didn't want to think of Maybelle and I sat at my desk reading *Popular Mechanics* or whittling at a toothbrush rack I was making. It seemed to me I was putting that girl out of my mind pretty well.

But you can't help what happens to you at night. That is what made things how they are now.

You see a few nights after Maybelle said those words to me I dreamed about her again. It was like that first time and I was squeezing Sucker's arm so tight I woke him up. He reached for my hand.

"Pete, what's the matter with you?"

All of a sudden I felt so mad my throat choked — at myself and the dream and Maybelle and Sucker and every single person I knew. I remembered all the times Maybelle had humiliated me and everything bad that had ever happened. It seemed to me for a second that nobody would ever like me but a sap like Sucker.

"Why is it we aren't buddies like we were before? Why —?"

"Shut your damn trap!" I threw off the cover and got up and turned on the light. He sat in the middle of the bed, his eyes blinking and scared.

There was something in me and I couldn't help myself. I don't think anybody ever gets that mad but once. Words came without me knowing what they would be. It was only afterward that I could remember each thing I said and see it all in a clear way.

"Why aren't we buddies? Because you're the dumbest slob I ever saw! Nobody cares anything about you! And just because I felt sorry for you sometimes and tried to act decent don't think I give a damn about a dumb-bunny like you!"

If I'd talked loud or hit him it wouldn't have been so bad.

But my voice was slow and like I was very calm. Sucker's mouth was part-way open and he looked as though he'd knocked his funny bone. His face was white and sweat came out on his forehead. He wiped it away with the back of his hand and for a minute his arm stayed raised that way as though he was holding something away from him.

"Don't you know a single thing? Haven't you ever been around at all? Why don't you get a girl friend instead of me? What kind of a sissy do you want to grow up to be anyway?"

I didn't know what was coming next. I couldn't help myself or think.

Sucker didn't move. He had on one of my pajama jackets and his neck stuck out skinny and small. His hair was damp on his forehead.

"Why do you always hang around me? Don't you know when you're not wanted?"

Afterward I could remember the change in Sucker's face. Slowly that blank look went away and he closed his mouth. His eyes got narrow and his fists shut. There had never been such a look on him before. It was like every second he was getting older. There was a hard look to his eyes you don't see usually in a kid. A drop of sweat rolled down his chin and he didn't notice. He just sat there with those eyes on me and he didn't speak and his face was hard and didn't move.

"No, you don't know when you're not wanted. You're too dumb. Just like your name — a dumb Sucker."

It was like something had busted inside me. I turned off the light and sat down in the chair by the window. My legs were shaking and I was so tired I could have bawled. The room was cold and dark. I sat there for a long time and smoked a squashed cigarette I had saved. Outside the yard was black and quiet. After a while I heard Sucker lie down.

I wasn't mad any more, only tired. It seemed awful to me that I had talked like that to a kid only twelve. I couldn't take it all in. I told myself I would go over to him and try to make it up. But I just sat there in the cold until a long time had passed.

I planned how I could straighten it out in the morning. Then, trying not to squeak the springs, I got back in bed.

Sucker was gone when I woke up the next day. And later when I wanted to apologize as I had planned he looked at me in this new hard way so that I couldn't say a word.

All of that was two or three months ago. Since then Sucker has grown faster than any boy I ever saw. He's almost as tall as I am and his bones have gotten heavier and bigger. He won't wear any of my old clothes any more and has bought his first pair of long pants—with some leather suspenders to hold them up. Those are just the changes that are easy to see and put into words.

Our room isn't mine at all any more. He's gotten up this gang of kids and they have a club. When they aren't digging trenches in some vacant lot and fighting they are always in my room. On the door there is some foolishness written in Mercurochrome saying "Woe to the Outsider who Enters" and signed with crossed bones and their secret initials. They have rigged up a radio and every afternoon it blares out music. Once as I was coming in I heard a boy telling something in a low voice about what he saw in the back of his big brother's automobile. I could guess what I didn't hear. "That's what her and my brother do. It's the truth—parked in the car." For a minute Sucker looked surprised and his face was almost like it used to be. Then he got hard and tough again. "Sure, dumbell. We know all that." They didn't notice me. Sucker began telling them how in two years he was planning to be a trapper in Alaska.

But most of the time Sucker stays by himself. It is worse when we are alone together in the room. He sprawls across the bed in those long corduroy pants with the suspenders and just stares at me with that hard, half-sneering look. I fiddle around my desk and can't get settled because of those eyes of his. And the thing is I just have to study because I've gotten three bad cards this term already. If I flunk English I can't graduate next year. I don't want to be a bum and I just have to get my mind on it. I don't care a flip for Maybelle or any particular girl any more and it's only this thing between Sucker and me that is the trouble now.

We never speak except when we have to before the family. I don't even want to call him Sucker any more and unless I forget I call him by his real name, Richard. At night I can't study with him in the room and I have to hang around the drugstore, smoking and doing nothing, with the fellows who loaf there.

More than anything I want to be easy in my mind again. And I miss the way Sucker and I were for a while in a funny, sad way that before this I never would have believed. But everything is so different that there seems to be nothing I can do to get it right. I've sometimes thought if we could have it out in a big fight that would help. But I can't fight him because he's four years younger. And another thing — sometimes this look in his eyes makes me almost believe that if Sucker could he would kill me.

JAMES HURST

The Scarlet Ibis

". . . pride is a wonderful, terrible thing, a seed that bears two vines, life and death."

It was in the clove of seasons, summer was dead but autumn had not yet been born, that the ibis lit in the bleeding tree. The flower garden was stained with rotting brown magnolia petals and ironweeds grew rank amid the purple phlox. The five o'clocks by the chimney still marked time, but the oriole nest in the elm was untenanted and rocked back and forth like an empty cradle. The last graveyard flowers were blooming, and their smell drifted across the cotton field and through every room of our house, speaking softly the names of our dead.

It's strange that all this is still so clear to me, now that that summer has long since fled and time has had its way. A grindstone stands where the bleeding tree stood, just outside the kitchen door, and now if an oriole sings in the elm, its song seems to die up in the leaves, a silvery dust. The flower garden is prim, the house a gleaming white, and the pale fence across the yard stands straight and spruce. But sometimes (like right now), as I sit in the cool, green-draped parlor, the grindstone begins to turn, and time with all its changes is ground away — and I remember Doodle.

Doodle was just about the craziest brother a boy ever had. Of course, he wasn't a crazy crazy like old Miss Leedie, who was in love with President Wilson and wrote him a letter every day, but was a nice crazy, like someone you meet in your dreams. He was born when I was six and was, from the outset, a disappointment. He seemed all head, with a tiny body which was red and shriveled like an old man's. Everybody thought he was going to die—everybody except Aunt Nicey, who had delivered him. She said he would live because he was born in a caul and cauls were made from Jesus' nightgown. Daddy had Mr. Heath, the carpenter, build a little mahogany coffin for him. But he didn't die, and when he was three months old Mama and Daddy decided they might as well name him. They named him William Armstrong, which was like tying a big tail on a small kite. Such a name sounds good only on a tombstone.

I thought myself pretty smart at many things, like holding my breath, running, jumping, or climbing the vines in Old Woman Swamp, and I wanted more than anything else someone to race to Horsehead Landing, someone to box with, and someone to perch with in the top fork of the great pine behind the barn, where across the fields and swamps you could see the sea. I wanted a brother. But Mama, crying, told me that even if William Armstrong lived, he would never do these things with me. He might not, she sobbed, even be "all there." He might, as long as he lived, lie on the rubber sheet in the center of the bed in the front bedroom where the white marquisette curtains billowed out in the afternoon sea breeze, rustling like palmetto fronds.

It was bad enough having an invalid brother, but having one who possibly was not all there was unbearable, so I began to make plans to kill him by smothering him with a pillow. However, one afternoon as I watched him, my head poked between the iron posts of the foot of the bed, he looked straight at me and grinned. I skipped through the rooms, down the echoing halls, shouting, "Mama, he smiled. He's all there! He's all there!" and he was.

When he was two, if you laid him on his stomach, he began to try to move himself, straining terribly. The doctor said that with his weak heart this strain would probably kill him, but it didn't. Trembling, he'd push himself up, turning first red, then a soft purple, and finally collapse back onto the bed like an old worn-out doll. I can still see Mama watching him, her hand pressed tight across her mouth, her eyes wide and unblinking. But he learned to crawl (it was his third winter), and we brought him out of the front bedroom, putting him on the rug before the fireplace. For the first time he became one of us.

As long as he lay all the time in bed, we called him William Armstrong, even though it was formal and sounded as if we were referring to one of our ancestors, but with his creeping around on the deerskin rug and beginning to talk, something had to be done about his name. It was I who renamed him. When he crawled, he crawled backwards, as if he were in reverse and couldn't change gears. If you called him, he'd turn around as if he were going in the other direction, then he'd back right up to you to be picked up. Crawling backward made him look like a doodlebug, so I began to call him Doodle, and in time even Mama and Daddy thought it was a better name than William Armstrong. Only Aunt Nicey disagreed. She said caul babies should be treated with special respect since they might turn out to be saints. Renaming my brother was perhaps the kindest thing I ever did for him, because nobody expects much from someone called Doodle.

Although Doodle learned to crawl, he showed no signs of walking, but he wasn't idle. He talked so much that we all quit listening to what he said. It was about this time that Daddy built him a go-cart and I had to pull him around. At first I just paraded him up and down the piazza, but then he started crying to be taken out into the yard and it ended up by my having to lug him wherever I went. If I so much as picked up my cap, he'd start crying to go with me and Mama would call from wherever she was, "Take Doodle with you."

He was a burden in many ways. The doctor had said that he mustn't get too excited, too hot, too cold, or too tired and that he must always be treated gently. A long list of don'ts went with him, all of which I ignored once we got out of the house. To discourage his coming with me, I'd run with him across the ends of the cotton rows and careen him around corners on two wheels. Sometimes I accidentally turned him over, but he never told Mama. His skin was very sensitive, and he had to wear a big straw hat whenever he went out. When the going got rough and he had to cling to the sides of the go-cart, the hat slipped all the way down over his ears. He was a sight. Finally, I could see I was licked. Doodle was my brother and he was going to cling to me forever, no matter what I did, so I dragged him across the burning cotton field to share with him the only beauty I knew, Old Woman Swamp. I pulled the go-cart through the saw-tooth fern, down into the green dimness where the palmetto fronds whispered by the stream. I lifted him out and set him down in the soft rubber grass beside a tall pine. His eyes were round with wonder as he gazed about him, and his little hands began to stroke the rubber grass. Then he began to cry.

"For heaven's sake, what's the matter?" I asked, annoyed.

"It's so pretty," he said. "So pretty, pretty, pretty."

After that day Doodle and I often went down into Old Woman Swamp. I would gather wildflowers, wild violets, honeysuckle, yellow jasmine, snakeflowers, and water lilies, and with wire grass we'd weave them into necklaces and crowns. We'd bedeck ourselves with our handiwork and loll about thus beautified, beyond the touch of the everyday world. Then when the slanted rays of the sun burned orange in the tops of the pines, we'd drop our jewels into the stream and watch them float away toward the sea.

There is within me (and with sadness I have watched it in others) a knot of cruelty borne by the stream of love, much as our blood sometimes bears the seed of our destruction, and at times I was mean to Doodle. One day I took him up to the barn loft and showed him his casket, telling him how we all had believed he would die. It was covered with a film of Paris green sprinkled to kill the rats, and screech owls had built a nest inside it.

Doodle studied the mahogany box for a long time, then said, "It's not mine."

"It is," I said. "And before I'll help you down from the loft, you're going to have to touch it."

"I won't touch it," he said sullenly.

"Then I'll leave you here by yourself," I threatened, and made as if I were going down.

Doodle was frightened of being left. "Don't go leave me, Brother," he cried, and he leaned toward the coffin. His hand, trembling, reached out, and when he touched the casket he screamed. A screech owl flapped out of the box into our faces, scaring us and covering us with Paris green. Doodle was paralyzed, so I put him on my shoulder and carried him down the ladder, and even when we were outside in the bright sunshine, he clung to me, crying, "Don't leave me. Don't leave me."

When Doodle was five years old, I was embarrassed at having a brother of that age who couldn't walk, so I set out to teach him. We were down in Old Woman Swamp and it was spring and the sick-sweet smell of bay flowers hung everywhere like a mournful song. "I'm going to teach you to walk, Doodle," I said.

He was sitting comfortably on the soft grass, leaning back against the pine. "Why?" he asked.

I hadn't expected such an answer. "So I won't have to haul you around all the time."

"I can't walk, Brother," he said.

"Who says so?" I demanded.

"Mama, the doctor — everybody."

"Oh, you can walk," I said, and I took him by the arms and stood him up. He collapsed onto the grass like a half-empty flour sack. It was as if he had no bones in his little legs.

"Don't hurt me, Brother," he warned.

"Shut up. I'm not going to hurt you. I'm going to teach you to walk." I heaved him up again, and again he collapsed.

This time he did not lift his face up out of the rubber grass. "I just can't do it. Let's make honeysuckle wreaths."

"Oh yes you can, Doodle," I said. "All you got to do is try. Now come on," and I hauled him up once more.

It seemed so hopeless from the beginning that it's a miracle I didn't give up. But all of us must have something or someone to be proud of, and Doodle had become mine. I did not know then that pride is a wonderful, terrible thing, a seed that bears two vines, life and death. Every day that summer we went to the pine beside the stream of Old Woman Swamp, and I put him on his feet at least a hundred times each afternoon. Occasionally I too became discouraged because it didn't seem as if he was trying, and I would say, "Doodle, don't you *want* to learn to walk?"

He'd nod his head, and I'd say, "Well, if you don't keep trying, you'll never learn." Then I'd paint for him a picture of us as old men, white-haired, him with a long white beard and me still pulling him around in the go-cart. This never failed to make him try again.

Finally one day, after many weeks of practicing, he stood alone for a few seconds. When he fell, I grabbed him in my arms and hugged him, our laughter pealing through the swamp like a ringing bell. Now we knew it could be done. Hope no longer hid in the dark palmetto thicket but perched like a cardinal in the lacy toothbrush tree, brilliantly visible. "Yes, yes," I cried, and he cried it too, and the grass beneath us was soft and the smell of the swamp was sweet.

With success so imminent, we decided not to tell anyone until he could actually walk. Each day, barring rain, we sneaked into Old Woman Swamp, and by cotton-picking time Doodle was ready to show what he could do. He still wasn't able to walk far, but we could wait no longer. Keeping a nice secret is very hard to do, like holding your breath. We chose to reveal all on October eighth, Doodle's sixth birthday, and for weeks ahead we mooned around the house, promising everybody a most spectacular surprise. Aunt Nicey said that, after so much talk, if we produced anything less tremendous than the Resurrection, she was going to be disappointed.

At breakfast on our chosen day, when Mama, Daddy, and Aunt Nicey were in the dining room, I brought Doodle to the door in the go-cart just as usual and had them turn their backs, making them cross their hearts and hope to die if they peeked. I helped Doodle up, and when he was standing alone I let them look. There wasn't a sound as Doodle walked slowly across the room and sat down at his place at the table. Then Mama began to cry and ran over to him, hugging him and kissing him. Daddy hugged him too, so I went to Aunt Nicey, who was thanks praying in the doorway, and began to waltz her around. We danced together quite well until she came down on my big toe with her brogans, hurting me so badly I thought I was crippled for life.

Doodle told them it was I who had taught him to walk, so everyone wanted to hug me, and I began to cry.

"What are you crying for?" asked Daddy, but I couldn't answer. They did not know that I did it for myself; that pride, whose slave I was, spoke to me louder than all their voices, and that Doodle walked only because I was ashamed of having a crippled brother.

Within a few months Doodle had learned to walk well and his go-cart was put up in the barn loft (it's still there) beside his little mahogany coffin. Now, when we roamed off together, resting often, we never turned back until our destination had been reached, and to help pass the time, we took up lying. From the beginning Doodle was a terrible liar and he got me in the habit. Had anyone stopped to listen to us, we would have been sent off to Dix Hill.

My lies were scary, involved, and usually pointless, but Doodle's were twice as crazy. People in his stories all had wings and flew wherever they wanted to go. His favorite lie was about a boy named Peter who had a pet peacock with a ten-foot tail. Peter wore a golden robe that glittered so brightly that when he walked through the sunflowers they turned away from the sun to face him. When Peter was ready to go to sleep, the peacock spread his magnificent tail, enfolding the boy gently like a closing go-to-sleep flower, burying him in the gloriously iridescent, rustling vortex. Yes, I must admit it. Doodle could beat me lying.

Doodle and I spent lots of time thinking about our future. We decided that when we were grown we'd live in Old Woman Swamp and pick dog-tongue for a living. Beside the stream, he planned, we'd build us a house of whispering leaves and the swamp birds would be our chickens. All day long (when we weren't gathering dog-tongue) we'd swing through the cypresses on the rope vines, and if it rained we'd huddle beneath an umbrella tree and play stickfrog. Mama and Daddy could come and live with us if they wanted to. He even came up with the idea that he could marry Mama and I could marry Daddy. Of course, I was old enough to know this wouldn't work out, but the picture he painted was so beautiful and serene that all I could do was whisper, yes, yes.

Once I had succeeded in teaching Doodle to walk, I began to believe in my own infallibility and I prepared a terrific development program for him, unknown to Mama and Daddy, of course. I would teach him to run, to swim, to climb trees, and to fight. He, too, now believed in my infallibility, so we set the deadline for these accomplishments less than a year away, when, it had been decided, Doodle could start to school.

That winter we didn't make much progress, for I was in school and Doodle suffered from one bad cold after another. But when spring came, rich and warm, we raised our sights again. Success lay at the end of summer like a pot of gold, and our campaign got off to a good start. On hot days, Doodle and I went down to Horsehead Landing and I gave him swimming lessons or showed him how to row a boat. Sometimes we descended into the cool greenness of Old Woman Swamp and climbed the rope vines or boxed scientifically beneath the pine where he had learned to walk. Promise hung about us like the leaves, and wherever we looked, ferns unfurled and birds broke into song.

That summer, the summer of 1918, was blighted. In May and June there was no rain and the crops withered, curled up, then died under the thirsty sun. One morning in July a hurricane came out of the east, tipping over the oaks in the yard and splitting the limbs of the elm trees. That afternoon it roared back out of the west, blew the fallen oaks around, snapping their roots and tearing them out of the earth like a hawk at the entrails of a chicken. Cotton bolls were wrenched from the stalks and lay like green walnuts in the valleys between the rows, while the cornfield leaned over uniformly so that the tassels touched the ground. Doodle and I followed Daddy out into the cotton field, where he stood, shoulders sagging, surveying the ruin. When his chin sank down onto his chest, we were frightened, and Doodle slipped his hand into mine. Suddenly Daddy straightened his shoulders, raised a giant knuckly fist, and with a voice that seemed to rumble out of the earth itself began cursing heaven, hell, the weather, and the Republican Party.

Doodle and I, prodding each other and giggling, went back to the house, knowing that everything would be all right.

And during that summer, strange names were heard through the house: Château-Thierry, Amiens, Soissons, and in her blessing at the supper table, Mama once said, "And bless the Pearsons, whose boy Joe was lost at Belleau Wood."

So we came to that clove of seasons. School was only a few weeks away, and Doodle was far behind schedule. He could barely clear the ground when climbing up the rope vines and his swimming was certainly not passable. We decided to double our efforts, to make that last drive and reach our pot of gold. I made him swim until he turned blue and row until he couldn't lift an oar. Wherever we went, I purposely walked fast, and although he kept up, his face turned red and his eyes became glazed. Once, he could go no further, so he collapsed on the ground and began to cry.

"Aw, come on, Doodle," I urged. "You can do it. Do you want to be different from everybody else when you start school?"

"Does it make any difference?"

"It certainly does," I said. "Now, come on," and I helped him up.

As we slipped through dog days, Doodle began to look feverish, and Mama felt his forehead, asking him if he felt ill. At night he didn't sleep well, and sometimes he had nightmares, crying out until I touched him and said, "Wake up, Doodle. Wake up."

It was Saturday noon, just a few days before school was to start. I should have already admitted defeat, but my pride wouldn't let me. The excitement of our program had now been gone for weeks, but still we kept on with a tired doggedness. It was too late to turn back, for we had both wandered too far into a net of expectations and had left no crumbs behind.

Daddy, Mama, Doodle, and I were seated at the dining-room table having lunch. It was a hot day, with all the windows and doors open in case a breeze should come. In the kitchen Aunt Nicey was humming softly. After a long silence, Daddy spoke. "It's so calm, I wouldn't be surprised if we had a storm this afternoon."

"I haven't heard a rain frog," said Mama, who believed in signs, as she served the bread around the table.

"I did," declared Doodle. "Down in the swamp."

"He didn't," I said contrarily.

"You did, eh?" said Daddy, ignoring my denial.

"I certainly did," Doodle reiterated, scowling at me over the top of his iced-tea glass, and we were quiet again.

Suddenly, from out in the yard, came a strange croaking noise. Doodle stopped eating, with a piece of bread poised ready for his mouth, his eyes popped round like two blue buttons. "What's that?" he whispered.

I jumped up, knocking over my chair, and had reached the door when Mama called, "Pick up the chair, sit down again, and say excuse me."

By the time I had done this, Doodle had excused himself and had slipped out into the yard. He was looking up into the bleeding tree. "It's a great big red bird!" he called.

The bird croaked loudly again, and Mama and Daddy came out into the yard. We shaded our eyes with our hands against the hazy glare of the sun and peered up through the still leaves. On the topmost branch a bird the size of a chicken, with scarlet feathers and long legs, was perched precariously. Its wings hung down loosely, and as we watched, a feather dropped away and floated slowly down through the green leaves.

"It's not even frightened of us," Mama said.

"It looks tired," Daddy added. "Or maybe sick."

Doodle's hands were clasped at his throat, and I had never seen him stand still so long. "What is it?" he asked.

Daddy shook his head. "I don't know, maybe it's —"

At that moment the bird began to flutter, but the wings were uncoördinated, and amid much flapping and a spray of flying feathers, it tumbled down, bumping through the limbs of the bleeding tree and landing at our feet with a thud. Its long, graceful neck jerked twice into an S, then straightened out, and the bird was still. A white veil came over the eyes and the long white beak unhinged. Its legs were crossed and its clawlike feet were delicately curved at rest. Even death did not mar its grace, for it lay on the earth like a broken vase of red flowers, and we stood around it, awed by its exotic beauty.

"It's dead," Mama said.

"What is it?" Doodle repeated.

"Go bring me the bird book," said Daddy.

I ran into the house and brought back the bird book. As we watched, Daddy thumbed through its pages. "It's a scarlet ibis," he said, pointing to a picture. "It lives in the tropics — South America to Florida. A storm must have brought it here."

Sadly, we all looked back at the bird. A scarlet ibis! How many miles it had traveled to die like this, in *our* yard, beneath the bleeding tree.

"Let's finish lunch," Mama said, nudging us back toward the dining room.

"I'm not hungry," said Doodle, and he knelt down beside the ibis.

"We've got peach cobbler for dessert," Mama tempted from the doorway.

Doodle remained kneeling. "I'm going to bury him."

"Don't you dare touch him," Mama warned. "There's no telling what disease he might have had."

"All right," said Doodle. "I won't."

Daddy, Mama, and I went back to the dining-room table, but we watched Doodle through the open door. He took out a piece of string from his pocket and, without touching the ibis, looped one end around its neck. Slowly, while singing softly *Shall We Gather at the River,* he carried the bird around to the front yard and dug a hole in the flower garden, next to the petunia bed. Now we were watching him through the front window, but he didn't know it. His awkwardness at digging the hole with a shovel whose handle was twice as long as he was made us laugh, and we covered our mouths with our hands so he wouldn't hear.

When Doodle came into the dining room, he found us seriously eating our cobbler. He was pale and lingered just inside the screen door. "Did you get the scarlet ibis buried?" asked Daddy.

Doodle didn't speak but nodded his head.

"Go wash your hands, and then you can have some peach cobbler," said Mama.

"I'm not hungry," he said.

"Dead birds is bad luck," said Aunt Nicey poking her head from the kitchen door. "Specially *red* dead birds!"

As soon as I had finished eating, Doodle and I hurried off to Horsehead Landing. Time was short, and Doodle still had a long way to go if he was going to keep up with the other boys when he started school. The sun, gilded with the yellow cast of autumn, still burned fiercely, but the dark green woods through which we passed were shady and cool. When we reached the landing, Doodle said he was too tired to swim, so we got into a skiff and floated down the creek with the tide. Far off in the marsh a rail was scolding, and over on the beach locusts were singing in the myrtle trees. Doodle did not speak and kept his head turned away, letting one hand trail limply in the water.

After we had drifted a long way, I put the oars in place and made Doodle row back against the tide. Black clouds began to gather in the southwest, and he kept watching them, trying to pull the oars a little faster. When we reached Horsehead Landing, lightning was playing across half the sky and thunder roared out, hiding even the sound of the sea. The sun disappeared and darkness descended, almost like night. Flocks of marsh crows flew by, heading inland to their roosting trees, and two egrets, squawking, arose from the oyster-rock shallows and careened away.

Doodle was both tired and frightened, and when he stepped from the skiff he collapsed onto the mud, sending an armada of fiddler crabs rustling off into the marsh grass. I helped him up, and as he wiped the mud off his trousers, he smiled at me ashamedly. He had failed and we both knew it, so we started back home, racing the storm. We never spoke (What are the words that can solder cracked pride?), but I knew he was watching me, watching for a sign of mercy. The lightning was near now, and from fear he walked so close behind me he kept stepping on my heels. The faster I walked, the faster he walked, so I began to run. The rain was coming, roaring through the pines, and then like a bursting Roman candle, a gum tree ahead of us was shattered by a bolt of lightning. When the deafening peal of thunder had died, and in the moment before the rain arrived, I heard Doodle, who had fallen behind, cry out, "Brother, Brother, don't leave me! Don't leave me!"

The knowledge that Doodle's and my plans had come to naught was bitter, and that streak of cruelty within me awakened. I ran as fast as I could, leaving him far behind with a wall of rain dividing us. The drops stung my face like nettles, and the wind flared the wet glistening leaves of the bordering trees. Soon I could hear his voice no more.

I hadn't run too far before I became tired, and the flood of childish spite evanesced as well. I stopped and waited for Doodle. The sound of rain was everywhere, but the wind had died and it fell straight down in parallel paths like ropes hanging from the sky. As I waited, I peered through the downpour, but no one came. Finally I went back and found him huddled beneath a red nightshade bush beside the road. He was sitting on the ground, his face buried in his arms, which were resting on his drawn-up knees. "Let's go, Doodle," I said.

He didn't answer, so I placed my hand on his forehead and lifted his head. Limply, he fell backwards onto the earth. He had been bleeding from the mouth, and his neck and the front of his shirt were stained a brilliant red.

"Doodle! Doodle!" I cried, shaking him, but there was no answer but the ropy rain. He lay very awkwardly, with his head thrown far back, making his vermilion neck appear unusually long and slim. His little legs, bent sharply at the knees, had never before seemed so fragile, so thin.

I began to weep, and the tear-blurred vision in red before me looked very familiar. "Doodle!" I screamed above the pounding storm and threw my body to the earth above his. For a long time, it seemed forever, I lay there crying, sheltering my fallen scarlet ibis from the heresy of rain.

SAKI

Tobermory

It was a chill, rain-washed afternoon of a late August day, that indefinite season when partridges are still in security or cold storage, and there is nothing to hunt — unless one is bounded on the north by the Bristol Channel, in which case one may lawfully gallop after fat red stags. Lady Blemley's house-party was not bounded on the north by the Bristol Channel, hence there was a full gathering of her guests round the tea-table on this particular afternoon. And, in spite of the blankness of the season and the triteness of the occasion, there was no trace in the company of that fatigued restlessness which means a dread of the pianola and a subdued hankering for auction bridge. The undisguised open-mouthed attention of the entire party was fixed on the homely negative personality of Mr. Cornelius Appin. Of all her guests, he was the one who had come to Lady Blemley with the vaguest reputation. Some one had said he was "clever," and he had got his invitation in the moderate expectation, on the part of his hostess, that some portion at least of his cleverness would be contributed to the general entertainment. Until tea-time that day she had been unable to discover in what direction, if any, his cleverness lay. He was neither a wit nor a croquet champion, a hypnotic force nor a begetter of amateur theatricals. Neither did his exterior suggest the sort of man in whom women are willing to pardon a generous measure of mental deficiency. He had subsided into mere Mr. Appin, and the Cornelius seemed a piece of transparent baptismal bluff. And now he was claiming to have launched on the world a discovery beside which the invention of gunpowder, of the printing-press, and of steam locomotion were inconsiderable trifles. Science had made bewildering strides in many directions during recent decades, but this thing seemed to belong to the domain of miracle rather than to scientific achievement.

"And do you really ask us to believe," Sir Wilfrid was saying, "that you have discovered a means for instructing animals in the art of human speech, and that dear old Tobermory has proved your first successful pupil?"

"It is a problem at which I have worked for the last seventeen years," said Mr. Appin, "but only during the last eight or nine months have I been rewarded with glimmerings of success. Of course I have experimented with thousands of animals, but latterly only with cats, those wonderful creatures which have assimilated themselves so marvellously with our civilization while retaining all their highly developed feral instincts. Here and there among cats one comes across an outstanding superior intellect, just as one does among the ruck of human beings, and when I made the acquaintance of Tobermory a week ago I saw at once that I was in contact with a 'Beyond-cat' of extraordinary intelligence. I had gone far along the road to success in recent experiments; with Tobermory, as you call him, I have reached the goal."

Mr. Appin concluded his remarkable statement in a voice which he strove to divest of a triumphant inflection. No one said "Rats," though Clovis's lips moved in a monosyllabic contortion which probably invoked those rodents of disbelief.

"And do you mean to say," asked Miss Resker, after a slight pause, "that you have taught Tobermory to say and understand easy sentences of one syllable?"

"My dear Miss Resker," said the wonder-worker patiently,

"one teaches little children and savages and backward adults in that piecemeal fashion; when one has once solved the problem of making a beginning with an animal of highly developed intelligence one has no need for those halting methods. Tobermory can speak our language with perfect correctness."

This time Clovis very distinctly said, "Beyond-rats!" Sir Wilfrid was more polite, but equally sceptical.

"Hadn't we better have the cat in and judge for ourselves?" suggested Lady Blemley.

Sir Wilfrid went in search of the animal, and the company settled themselves down to the languid expectation of witnessing some more or less adroit drawing-room ventriloquism.

In a minute Sir Wilfrid was back in the room, his face white beneath its tan and his eyes dilated with excitement.

"By Gad, it's true!"

His agitation was unmistakably genuine, and his hearers started forward in a thrill of awakened interest.

Collapsing into an armchair he continued breathlessly: "I found him dozing in the smoking-room, and called out to him to come for his tea. He blinked at me in his usual way, and I said, 'Come on, Toby; don't keep us waiting'; and, by Gad! he drawled out in a most horribly natural voice that he'd come when he dashed well pleased! I nearly jumped out of my skin!"

Appin had preached to absolutely incredulous hearers; Sir Wilfrid's statement carried instant conviction. A Babel-like chorus of startled exclamation arose, amid which the scientist sat mutely enjoying the first fruit of his stupendous discovery.

In the midst of the clamour Tobermory entered the room and made his way with velvet tread and studied unconcern across the group seated round the tea-table.

A sudden hush of awkwardness and constraint fell on the company. Somehow there seemed an element of embarrassment in addressing on equal terms a domestic cat of acknowledged mental ability.

"Will you have some milk, Tobermory?" asked Lady Blemley in a rather strained voice.

"I don't mind if I do," was the response, couched in a tone of even indifference. A shiver of suppressed excitement went through the listeners, and Lady Blemley might be excused for pouring out the saucerful of milk rather unsteadily.

"I'm afraid I've spilt a good deal of it," she said apologetically.

"After all, it's not my Axminster," was Tobermory's rejoinder.

Another silence fell on the group, and then Miss Resker, in her best district-visitor manner, asked if the human language had been difficult to learn. Tobermory looked squarely at her for a moment and then fixed his gaze serenely on the middle distance. It was obvious that boring questions lay outside his scheme of life.

"What do you think of human intelligence?" asked Mavis Pellington lamely.

"Of whose intelligence in particular?" asked Tobermory coldly.

"Oh, well, mine for instance," said Mavis, with a feeble laugh.

"You put me in an embarrassing position," said Tobermory, whose tone and attitude certainly did not suggest a shred of embarrassment. "When your inclusion in this house-party was suggested Sir Wilfrid protested that you were the most brainless woman of his acquaintance, and that there was a wide distinction between hospitality and the care of the feeble-minded. Lady Blemley replied that your lack of brain-power was the precise quality which had earned you your invitation, as you were the only person she could think of who might be idiotic enough to buy their old car. You know, the one they call 'The Envy of Sisyphus,' because it goes quite nicely up-hill if you push it."

Lady Blemley's protestations would have had greater effect if she had not casually suggested to Mavis only that morning that the car in question would be just the thing for her down at her Devonshire home.

Major Barfield plunged in heavily to effect a diversion.

"How about your carryings-on with the tortoise-shell puss up at the stables, eh?"

The moment he had said it every one realized the blunder.

"One does not usually discuss these matters in public," said Tobermory frigidly. "From a slight observation of your ways since you've been in this house I should imagine you'd find it inconvenient if I were to shift the conversation on to your own little affairs."

The panic which ensued was not confined to the Major.

"Would you like to go and see if cook has got your dinner ready?" suggested Lady Blemley hurriedly, affecting to ignore the fact that it wanted at least two hours to Tobermory's dinner-time.

"Thanks," said Tobermory, "not quite so soon after my tea. I don't want to die of indigestion."

"Cats have nine lives, you know," said Sir Wilfrid heartily.

"Possibly," answered Tobermory; "but only one liver."

"Adelaide!" said Mrs. Cornett, "do you mean to encourage that cat to go out and gossip about us in the servants' hall?"

The panic had indeed become general. A narrow ornamental balustrade ran in front of most of the bedroom windows at the Towers, and it was recalled with dismay that this had formed a favourite promenade for Tobermory at all hours, whence he could watch the pigeons — and heaven knew what else besides. If he intended to become reminiscent in his present out-spoken strain the effect would be something more than disconcerting. Mrs. Cornett, who spent much time at her toilet table, and whose complexion was reputed to be of a nomadic though punctual disposition, looked as ill at ease as the Major. Miss Scrawen, who wrote fiercely sensuous poetry and led a blameless life, merely displayed irritation; if you are methodical and virtuous in private you don't necessarily want every one to know it. Bertie van Tahn, who was so depraved at seventeen that he had long ago given up trying to be any worse, turned a dull shade of gardenia white, but he did not commit the error of dashing out of the room like Odo Finsberry, a young gentleman who was understood to be reading for the Church and who was possibly disturbed at the thought of scandals he might hear concerning other people. Clovis had the presence of mind to maintain a composed exterior; privately he was calculating how long it would take to procure a box of fancy mice through the agency of the *Exchange and Mart* as a species of hush-money.

Even in a delicate situation like the present, Agnes Resker could not endure to remain too long in the background.

"Why did I ever come down here?" she asked dramatically.

Tobermory immediately accepted the opening.

"Judging by what you said to Mrs. Cornett on the croquet-lawn yesterday, you were out for food. You described the Blemleys as the dullest people to stay with that you knew, but said they were clever enough to employ a first-rate cook; otherwise they'd find it difficult to get any one to come down a second time."

"There's not a word of truth in it! I appeal to Mrs. Cornett——" exclaimed the discomfited Agnes.

"Mrs. Cornett repeated your remark afterwards to Bertie van Tahn," continued Tobermory, "and said, 'That woman is a regular Hunger Marcher; she'd go anywhere for four square meals a day,' and Bertie van Tahn said——"

At this point the chronicle mercifully ceased. Tobermory had caught a glimpse of the big yellow Tom from the Rectory working his way through the shrubbery towards the stable wing. In a flash he had vanished through the open French window.

With the disappearance of his too brilliant pupil Cornelius Appin found himself beset by a hurricane of bitter upbraiding, anxious inquiry, and frightened entreaty. The responsibility for the situation lay with him, and he must prevent matters from becoming worse. Could Tobermory impart his dangerous gift to other cats? was the first question he had to answer. It was possible, he replied, that he might have initiated his intimate friend the stable puss into his new accomplishment, but it was unlikely that his teaching could have taken a wider range as yet.

"Then," said Mrs. Cornett, "Tobermory may be a valuable cat and a great pet; but I'm sure you'll agree, Adelaide, that both he and the stable cat must be done away with without delay."

"You don't suppose I've enjoyed the last quarter of an hour, do you?" said Lady Blemley bitterly. "My husband and I are very fond of Tobermory — at least, we were before this horrible accomplishment was infused into him; but now, of course, the only thing is to have him destroyed as soon as possible."

"We can put some strychnine in the scraps he always gets at dinner-time," said Sir Wilfrid, "and I will go and drown the stable cat myself. The coachman will be very sore at losing his pet, but I'll say a very catching form of mange has broken out in both cats and we're afraid of it spreading to the kennels."

"But my great discovery!" expostulated Mr. Appin; "after all my years of research and experiment——"

"You can go and experiment on the short-horns at the farm, who are under proper control," said Mrs. Cornett, "or the elephants at the Zoological Gardens. They're said to be highly intelligent, and they have this recommendation, that they don't come creeping about our bedrooms and under chairs, and so forth."

An archangel ecstatically proclaiming the Millennium, and finding that it clashed unpardonably with Henley and would have to be indefinitely postponed, could hardly have felt more crestfallen than Cornelius Appin at the reception of his wonderful achievement. Public opinion, however, was against him — in fact, had the general voice been consulted on the subject it is probable that a strong minority vote would have been in favor of including him in the strychnine diet.

Defective train arrangements and a nervous desire to see matters brought to a finish prevented an immediate dispersal of the party, but dinner that evening was not a social success. Sir Wilfrid had had rather a trying time with the stable cat and subsequently with the coachman. Agnes Resker ostentatiously limited her repast to a morsel of dry toast, which she bit as though it were a personal enemy; while Mavis Pellington maintained a vindictive silence throughout the meal. Lady Blemley kept up a flow of what she hoped was conversation, but her attention was fixed on the doorway. A plateful of carefully dosed fish scraps was in readiness on the sideboard, but sweets and savoury and dessert went their way, and no Tobermory appeared either in the dining-room or kitchen.

The sepulchral dinner was cheerful compared with the subsequent vigil in the smoking-room. Eating and drinking had at least supplied a distraction and cloak to the prevailing embarrassment. Bridge was out of the question in the general tension of nerves and tempers, and after Odo Finsberry had given a lugubrious rendering of "Melisande in the Wood" to a frigid audience, music was tacitly avoided. At eleven the servants went to bed, announcing that the small window in the pantry had been left open as usual for Tobermory's private use. The guests read steadily through the current batch of magazines, and fell back gradually on the "Badminton Library" and bound volumes of *Punch*. Lady Blemley made periodic visits to the pantry, returning each time with an expression of listless depression which forestalled questioning.

At two o'clock Clovis broke the dominating silence.

"He won't turn up tonight. He's probably in the local newspaper office at the present moment, dictating the first instalment of his reminiscences. Lady What's-her-name's book won't be in it. It will be the event of the day."

Having made this contribution to the general cheerfulness, Clovis went to bed. At long intervals the various members of the house-party followed his example.

The servants taking round the early tea made a uniform announcement in reply to a uniform question. Tobermory had not returned.

Breakfast was, if anything, a more unpleasant function than dinner had been, but before its conclusion the situation was relieved. Tobermory's corpse was brought in from the shrubbery, where a gardener had just discovered it. From the bites on his throat and the yellow fur which coated his claws it was evident that he had fallen in unequal combat with the big Tom from the Rectory.

By midday most of the guests had quitted the Towers, and after lunch Lady Blemley had sufficiently recovered her spirits to write an extremely nasty letter to the Rectory about the loss of her valuable pet.

Tobermory had been Appin's one successful pupil, and he was destined to have no successor. A few weeks later an elephant in the Dresden Zoological Garden, which had shown no previous signs of irritability, broke loose and killed an Englishman who had apparently been teasing it. The victim's name was variously reported in the papers as Oppin and Eppelin, but his front name was faithfully rendered Cornelius.

"If he was trying German irregular verbs on the poor beast," said Clovis, "he deserved all he got."

SHIRLEY JACKSON

After You, My Dear Alphonse

Mrs. Wilson was just taking the gingerbread out of the oven when she heard Johnny outside talking to someone.

"Johnny," she called, "you're late. Come in and get your lunch."

"Just a minute, Mother," Johnny said. "After you, my dear Alphonse."

"After *you,* my dear Alphonse," another voice said.

"No, after *you,* my dear Alphonse," Johnny said.

Mrs. Wilson opened the door. "Johnny," she said, "you come in this minute and get your lunch. You can play after you've eaten."

Johnny came in after her, slowly. "Mother," he said, "I brought Boyd home for lunch with me."

"Boyd?" Mrs. Wilson thought for a moment. "I don't believe I've met Boyd. Bring him in, dear, since you've invited him. Lunch is ready."

"Boyd!" Johnny yelled. "Hey, Boyd, come on in!"

"I'm coming. Just got to unload this stuff."

"Well, hurry, or my mother'll be sore."

"Johnny, that's not very polite to either your friend or your mother," Mrs. Wilson said. "Come sit down, Boyd."

As she turned to show Boyd where to sit, she saw he was a Negro boy, smaller than Johnny but about the same age. His arms were loaded with split kindling wood. "Where'll I put this stuff, Johnny?" he asked.

Mrs. Wilson turned to Johnny. "Johnny," she said, "what did you make Boyd do? What is that wood?"

"Dead Japanese," Johnny said mildly. "We stand them in the ground and run over them with tanks."

"How do you do, Mrs. Wilson?" Boyd said.

"How do you do, Boyd? You shouldn't let Johnny make you carry all that wood. Sit down now and eat lunch, both of you."

"Why shouldn't he carry the wood, Mother? It's his wood. We got it at his place."

"Johnny," Mrs. Wilson said, "go on and eat your lunch."

"Sure," Johnny said. He held out the dish of scrambled eggs to Boyd. "After you, my dear Alphonse."

"After *you,* my dear Alphonse," Boyd said.

"After *you,* my dear Alphonse," Johnny said. They began to giggle.

"Are you hungry, Boyd?" Mrs. Wilson asked.

"Yes, Mrs. Wilson."

"Well, don't you let Johnny stop you. He always fusses about eating, so you just see that you get a good lunch. There's plenty of food here for you to have all you want."

"Thank you, Mrs. Wilson."

"Come on, Alphonse," Johnny said. He pushed half the scrambled eggs on to Boyd's plate. Boyd watched while Mrs. Wilson put a dish of stewed tomatoes beside his plate.

"Boyd don't eat tomatoes, do you, Boyd?" Johnny said.

"*Doesn't* eat tomatoes, Johnny. And just because you don't like them, don't say that about Boyd. Boyd will eat *anything.*"

"Bet he won't," Johnny said, attacking his scrambled eggs.

"Boyd wants to grow up and be a big strong man so he can work hard," Mrs. Wilson said. "I'll bet Boyd's father eats stewed tomatoes."

"My father eats anything he wants to," Boyd said.

"So does mine," Johnny said. "Sometimes he doesn't eat hardly anything. He's a little guy, though. Wouldn't hurt a flea."

"Mine's a little guy too," Boyd said.

"I'll bet he's strong, though," Mrs. Wilson said. She hesitated. "Does he . . . work?"

"Sure," Johnny said. "Boyd's father works in a factory."

"There, you see?" Mrs. Wilson said. "And he certainly has to be strong to do that — all that lifting and carrying at a factory."

"Boyd's father doesn't have to," Johnny said. "He's a foreman."

Mrs. Wilson felt defeated. "What does your mother do, Boyd?"

"My mother?" Boyd was surprised. "She takes care of us kids."

"Oh. She doesn't work, then?"

"Why should she?" Johnny said through a mouthful of eggs. "You don't work."

"You really don't want any stewed tomatoes, Boyd?"

"No, thank you, Mrs. Wilson," Boyd said.

"No, thank you, Mrs. Wilson, no, thank you, Mrs. Wilson, no, thank you, Mrs. Wilson," Johnny said. "Boyd's sister's going to work, though. She's going to be a teacher."

"That's a very fine attitude for her to have, Boyd." Mrs. Wilson restrained an impulse to pat Boyd on the head. "I imagine you're all very proud of her?"

"I guess so," Boyd said.

"What about all your other brothers and sisters? I guess all of you want to make just as much of yourselves as you can."

"There's only me and Jean," Boyd said. "I don't know yet what I want to be when I grow up."

"We're going to be tank drivers, Boyd and me," Johnny said. "Zoom." Mrs. Wilson caught Boyd's glass of milk as Johnny's napkin ring, suddenly transformed into a tank, plowed heavily across the table.

"Look, Johnny," Boyd said. "Here's a foxhole. I'm shooting at you."

Mrs. Wilson, with the speed born of long experience, took the gingerbread off the shelf and placed it carefully between the tank and the foxhole.

"Now eat as much as you want to, Boyd," she said. "I want to see you get filled up."

"Boyd eats a lot, but not as much as I do," Johnny said. "I'm bigger than he is."

"You're not much bigger," Boyd said. "I can beat you running."

Mrs. Wilson took a deep breath. "Boyd," she said. Both boys turned to her. "Boyd, Johnny has some suits that are a little too small for him, and a winter coat. It's not new, of course, but there's lots of wear in it still. And I have a few dresses that your mother or sister could probably use. Your mother can make them over into lots of things for all of you, and I'd be very happy to give them to you. Suppose before you leave I make up a big bundle and then you and Johnny can take it over to your mother right away . . ." Her voice trailed off as she saw Boyd's puzzled expression.

"But I have plenty of clothes, thank you," he said. "And I don't think my mother knows how to sew very well, and anyhow I guess we buy about everything we need. Thank you very much, though."

"We don't have time to carry that old stuff around, Mother," Johnny said. "We got to play tanks with the kids today."

Mrs. Wilson lifted the plate of gingerbread off the table as Boyd was about to take another piece. "There are many little boys like you, Boyd, who would be very grateful for the clothes someone was kind enough to give them."

"Boyd will take them if you want him to, Mother," Johnny said.

"I didn't mean to make you mad, Mrs. Wilson," Boyd said.

"Don't think I'm angry, Boyd. I'm just disappointed in you, that's all. Now let's not say anything more about it."

She began clearing the plates off the table, and Johnny took Boyd's hand and pulled him to the door. " 'Bye, Mother," Johnny said. Boyd stood for a minute, staring at Mrs. Wilson's back.

"After you, my dear Alphonse," Johnny said, holding the door open.

"Is your mother still mad?" Mrs. Wilson heard Boyd ask in a low voice.

"I don't know," Johnny said. "She's screwy sometimes."

"So's mine," Boyd said. He hesitated. "After *you*, my dear Alphonse."

ERNEST HEMINGWAY

Old Man At the Bridge

An old man with steel rimmed spectacles and very dusty clothes sat by the side of the road. There was a pontoon bridge across the river and carts, trucks, and men, women and children were crossing it. The mule-drawn carts staggered up the steep bank from the bridge with soldiers helping push against the spokes of the wheels. The trucks ground up and away heading out of it all and the peasants plodded along in the ankle deep dust. But the old man sat there without moving. He was too tired to go any farther.

It was my business to cross the bridge, explore the bridgehead beyond and find out to what point the enemy had advanced. I did this and returned over the bridge. There were not so many carts now and very few people on foot, but the old man was still there.

"Where do you come from?" I asked him.

"From San Carlos," he said, and smiled.

That was his native town and so it gave him pleasure to mention it and he smiled.

"I was taking care of animals," he explained.

"Oh," I said, not quite understanding.

"Yes," he said, "I stayed, you see, taking care of animals. I was the last one to leave the town of San Carlos."

He did not look like a shepherd nor a herdsman and I looked at his black dusty clothes and his gray dusty face and his steel rimmed spectacles and said, "What animals were they?"

"Various animals," he said, and shook his head. "I had to leave them."

I was watching the bridge and the African looking country of the Ebro Delta and wondering how long now it would be before we would see the enemy, and listening all the while for the first noises that would signal that ever mysterious event called contact, and the old man still sat there.

"What animals were they?" I asked.

"There were three animals altogether," he explained. "There were two goats and a cat and then there were four pairs of pigeons."

"And you had to leave them?" I asked.

"Yes. Because of the artillery. The captain told me to go because of the artillery."

"And you have no family?" I asked, watching the far end of the bridge where a few last carts were hurrying down the slope of the bank.

"No," he said, "only the animals I stated. The cat, of course, will be all right. A cat can look out for itself, but I cannot think what will become of the others."

"What politics have you?" I asked.

"I am without politics," he said. "I am seventy-six years old. I have come twelve kilometers now and I think now I can go no further."

"This is not a good place to stop," I said. "If you can make it, there are trucks up the road where it forks for Tortosa."

"I will wait a while," he said, "and then I will go. Where do the trucks go?"

"Towards Barcelona," I told him.

"I know no one in that direction," he said, "but thank you very much. Thank you again very much."

He looked at me very blankly and tiredly, then said, having

to share his worry with some one, "The cat will be all right, I am sure. There is no need to be unquiet about the cat. But the others. Now what do you think about the others?"

"Why they'll probably come through it all right."

"You think so?"

"Why not," I said, watching the far bank where now there were no carts.

"But what will they do under the artillery when I was told to leave because of the artillery?"

"Did you leave the dove cage unlocked?" I asked.

"Yes."

"Then they'll fly."

"Yes, certainly they'll fly. But the others. It's better not to think about the others," he said.

"If you are rested I would go," I urged. "Get up and try to walk now."

"Thank you," he said and got to his feet, swayed from side to side and then sat down backwards in the dust.

"I was taking care of animals," he said dully, but no longer to me. "I was only taking care of animals."

There was nothing to do about him. It was Easter Sunday and the Fascists were advancing toward the Ebro. It was a gray overcast day with a low ceiling so their planes were not up. That and the fact that cats know how to look after themselves was all the good luck that old man would ever have.

PHILIP ROTH

The Conversion Of the Jews

You're a real one for opening your mouth in the first place," Itzie said. "What do you open your mouth all the time for?"

"I didn't bring it up, Itz, I didn't," Ozzie said.

"What do you care about Jesus Christ for anyway?"

"I didn't bring up Jesus Christ. He did. I didn't even know what he was talking about. Jesus is historical, he kept saying. Jesus is historical." Ozzie mimicked the monumental voice of Rabbi Binder.

"Jesus was a person that lived like you and me," Ozzie continued. "That's what Binder said—"

"Yeah? . . . So what! What do I give two cents whether he lived or not. And what do you gotta open your mouth!" Itzie Lieberman favored closed-mouthedness, especially when it came to Ozzie Freedman's questions. Mrs. Freedman had to see Rabbi Binder twice before about Ozzie's questions and this Wednesday at four-thirty would be the third time. Itzie preferred to keep *his* mother in the kitchen; he settled for behind-the-back subtleties such as gestures, faces, snarls and other less delicate barnyard noises.

"He was a real person, Jesus, but he wasn't like God, and we don't believe he is God." Slowly, Ozzie was explaining Rabbi Binder's position to Itzie, who had been absent from Hebrew School the previous afternoon.

"The Catholics," Itzie said helpfully, "they believe in Jesus Christ, that he's God." Itzie Lieberman used "the Catholics" in its broadest sense — to include the Protestants.

Ozzie received Itzie's remark with a tiny head bob, as though it were a footnote, and went on. "His mother was Mary, and his father probably was Joseph," Ozzie said. "But the New Testament says his real father was God."

"His *real* father?"

"Yeah," Ozzie said, "that's the big thing, his father's supposed to be God."

"Bull."

"That's what Rabbi Binder says, that it's impossible —"

"Sure it's impossible. That stuff's all bull. To have a baby you gotta get laid," Itzie theologized. "Mary hadda get laid."

"That's what Binder says: 'The only way a woman can have a baby is to have intercourse with a man.' "

"He said *that,* Ozz?" For a moment it appeared that Itzie had put the theological question aside. "He said that, intercourse?" A little curled smile shaped itself in the lower half of Itzie's face like a pink mustache. "What you guys do, Ozz, you laugh or something?"

"I raised my hand."

"Yeah? Whatja say?"

"That's when I asked the question."

Itzie's face lit up. "Whatja ask about — intercourse?"

"No, I asked the question about God, how if He could create the heaven and earth in six days, and make all the animals and the fish and the light in six days — the light especially, that's what always gets me, that He could make the light. Making fish and animals, that's pretty good —"

"That's damn good." Itzie's appreciation was honest but unimaginative: it was as though God had just pitched a one-hitter.

"But making light . . . I mean when you think about it, it's really something," Ozzie said. "Anyway, I asked Binder if He could make all that in six days, and He could *pick* the six days He wanted right out of nowhere, why couldn't He let a woman have a baby without having intercourse."

"You said intercourse, Ozz, to Binder?"

"Yeah."

"Right in class?"

"Yeah."

Itzie smacked the side of his head.

"I mean, no kidding around," Ozzie said, "that'd really be nothing. After all that other stuff, that'd practically be nothing."

Itzie considered a moment. "What'd Binder say?"

"He started all over again explaining how Jesus was historical and how he lived like you and me but he wasn't God. So I said I under*stood* that. What I wanted to know was different."

What Ozzie wanted to know was always different. The first time he had wanted to know how Rabbi Binder could call the Jews "The Chosen People" if the Declaration of Independence claimed all men to be created equal. Rabbi Binder tried to distinguish for him between political equality and spiritual legitimacy, but what Ozzie wanted to know, he insisted vehemently, was different. That was the first time his mother had to come.

Then there was the plane crash. Fifty-eight people had been killed in a plane crash at La Guardia. In studying a casualty list in the newspaper his mother had discovered among the list of those dead eight Jewish names (his grandmother had nine but she counted Miller as a Jewish name); because of the eight she said the plane crash was "a tragedy." During free-discussion time on Wednesday Ozzie had brought to Rabbi Binder's attention this matter of "some of his relations" always picking out the Jewish names. Rabbi Binder had begun to explain cultural unity and some other things when Ozzie stood up at his seat and said that what he wanted to know was different. Rabbi Binder insisted that he sit down and it was then that Ozzie shouted that he wished all fifty-eight were Jews. That was the second time his mother came.

"And he kept explaining about Jesus being historical, and so I kept asking him. No kidding, Itz, he was trying to make me look stupid."

"So what he finally do?"

"Finally he starts screaming that I was deliberately simple-minded and a wise guy, and that my mother had to come, and this was the last time. And that I'd never get bar-mitzvahed if he could help it. Then, Itz, then he starts talking in that voice like a statue, real slow and deep, and he says that I better think over what I said about the Lord. He told me to go to his office and think it over." Ozzie leaned his body towards Itzie. "Itz, I thought it over for a solid hour, and now I'm convinced God could do it."

Ozzie had planned to confess his latest transgression to his mother as soon as she came home from work. But it was a Friday night in November and already dark, and when Mrs. Freedman came through the door she tossed off her coat, kissed Ozzie quickly on the face, and went to the kitchen table to light the three yellow candles, two for the Sabbath and one for Ozzie's father.

When his mother lit the candles she would move her two arms slowly towards her, dragging them through the air, as though persuading people whose minds were half made up. And her eyes would get glassy with tears. Even when his father was alive Ozzie remembered that her eyes had gotten glassy, so it didn't have anything to do with his dying. It had something to do with lighting the candles.

As she touched the flaming match to the unlit wick of a Sabbath candle, the phone rang, and Ozzie, standing only a foot from it, plucked it off the receiver and held it muffled to his chest. When his mother lit candles Ozzie felt there should be no noise; even breathing, if you could manage it, should be softened. Ozzie pressed the phone to his breast and watched his mother dragging whatever she was dragging, and he felt his own eyes get glassy. His mother was a round, tired, gray-haired penguin of a woman whose gray skin had begun to feel the tug of gravity and the weight of her own history. Even when she was dressed up she didn't look like a chosen person. But when she lit candles she looked like something better; like a woman who knew momentarily that God could do anything.

After a few mysterious minutes she was finished. Ozzie hung up the phone and walked to the kitchen table where she was beginning to lay the two places for the four-course Sabbath meal. He told her that she would have to see Rabbi Binder next Wednesday at four-thirty, and then he told her why. For the first time in their life together she hit Ozzie across the face with her hand.

All through the chopped liver and chicken soup part of the dinner Ozzie cried; he didn't have any appetite for the rest.

On Wednesday, in the largest of the three basement classrooms of the synagogue, Rabbi Marvin Binder, a tall, handsome, broad-shouldered man of thirty with thick strong-fibered black hair, removed his watch from his pocket and saw that it was four o'clock. At the rear of the room Yakov Blotnik, the seventy-one-year-old custodian, slowly polished the large window, mumbling to himself, unaware that it was four o'clock or six o'clock, Monday or Wednesday. To most of the students Yakov Blotnik's mumbling, along with his brown curly beard, scythe nose, and two heel-trailing black cats, made of him an object of wonder, a foreigner, a relic, towards whom they were alternately fearful and disrespectful. To Ozzie the mumbling had always seemed a monotonous, curious prayer; what made it curious was that old Blotnik had been mumbling so steadily for so many years, Ozzie suspected he had memorized the prayers and forgotten all about God.

"It is now free-discussion time," Rabbi Binder said. "Feel free to talk about any Jewish matter at all — religion, family, politics, sports —"

There was silence. It was a gusty, clouded November afternoon and it did not seem as though there ever was or could be a thing called baseball. So nobody this week said a word about that hero from the past, Hank Greenberg — which limited free discussion considerably.

And the soul-battering Ozzie Freedman had just received from Rabbi Binder had imposed its limitation. When it was Ozzie's turn to read aloud from the Hebrew book the rabbi had asked him petulantly why he didn't read more rapidly. He was showing no progress. Ozzie said he could read faster but that if he did he was sure not to understand what he was reading. Nevertheless, at the rabbi's repeated suggestion Ozzie tried, and showed a great talent, but in the midst of a long passage he stopped short and said he didn't understand a word he was reading, and started in again at a drag-footed pace. Then came the soul-battering.

Consequently when free-discussion time rolled around none of the students felt too free. The rabbi's invitation was answered only by the mumbling of feeble old Blotnik.

"Isn't there anything at all you would like to discuss?" Rabbi Binder asked again, looking at his watch. "No questions or comments?"

There was a small grumble from the third row. The rabbi requested that Ozzie rise and give the rest of the class the advantage of his thought.

Ozzie rose. "I forget it now," he said, and sat down in his place.

Rabbi Binder advanced a seat towards Ozzie and poised himself on the edge of the desk. It was Itzie's desk and the rabbi's frame only a dagger's-length away from his face snapped him to sitting attention.

"Stand up again, Oscar," Rabbi Binder said calmly, "and try to assemble your thoughts."

Ozzie stood up. All his classmates turned in their seats and watched as he gave an unconvincing scratch to his forehead.

"I can't assemble any," he announced, and plunked himself down.

"Stand up!" Rabbi Binder advanced from Itzie's desk to the one directly in front of Ozzie; when the rabbinical back was turned Itzie gave it five fingers off the tip of his nose, causing a small titter in the room. Rabbi Binder was too absorbed in squelching Ozzie's nonsense once and for all to bother with titters. "Stand up, Oscar. What's your question about?"

Ozzie pulled a word out of the air. It was the handiest word. "Religion."

"Oh, now you remember?"

"Yes."

"What is it?"

Trapped, Ozzie blurted the first thing that came to him. "Why can't He make anything He wants to make?"

As Rabbi Binder prepared an answer, a final answer, Itzie, ten feet behind him, raised one finger on his left hand, gestured it meaningfully towards the rabbi's back, and brought the house down.

Binder twisted quickly to see what had happened and in the midst of the commotion Ozzie shouted into the rabbi's back what he couldn't have shouted to his face. It was a loud, toneless sound that had the timbre of something stored inside for about six days. "You don't know! You don't know anything about God!"

The rabbi spun back towards Ozzie. "What?"

"You don't know — you don't —"

"Apologize, Oscar, apologize!" It was a threat.

"You don't —"

Rabbi Binder's hand flicked out at Ozzie's cheek. Perhaps it had only been meant to clamp the boy's mouth shut, but Ozzie ducked and the palm caught him squarely on the nose.

The blood came in a short, red spurt on to Ozzie's shirt front.

The next moment was all confusion. Ozzie screamed, "You bastard, you bastard!" and broke for the classroom door. Rabbi Binder lurched a step backwards, as though his own blood had started flowing violently in the opposite direction, then gave a clumsy lurch forward and bolted out the door after Ozzie. The class followed after the rabbi's huge blue-suited back, and before old Blotnik could turn from his window, the room was empty and everyone was headed full speed up the three flights leading to the roof.

If one should compare the light of day to the life of man: sunrise to birth; sunset — the dropping down over the edge — to death; then as Ozzie Freedman wiggled through the trapdoor of the synagogue roof, his feet kicking backwards bronco-style at Rabbi Binder's outstretched arms — at that moment the day was fifty years old. As a rule, fifty or fifty-five reflects accurately the age of late afternoons in November, for it is in that month, during those hours, that one's awareness of light seems no longer a matter of seeing, but of hearing: light begins clicking away. In fact, as Ozzie locked shut the trapdoor in the rabbi's face, the sharp click of the bolt into the lock might momentarily have been mistaken for the sound of the heavier gray that had just throbbed through the sky.

With all his weight Ozzie kneeled on the locked door; any instant he was certain that Rabbi Binder's shoulder would fling it open, splintering the wood into shrapnel and catapulting his body into the sky. But the door did not move and below him he heard only the rumble of feet, first loud then dim, like thunder rolling away.

A question shot through his brain. "Can this be *me?*" For a thirteen-year-old who had just labeled his religious leader a bastard, twice, it was not an improper question. Louder and louder the question came to him — "Is it me? It is me?" — until he discovered himself no longer kneeling, but racing crazily towards the edge of the roof, his eyes crying, his throat screaming, and his arms flying everywhichway as though not his own.

"Is it me? Is it me Me ME ME ME! It has to be me — but is it!"

It is the question a thief must ask himself the night he jimmies open his first window, and it is said to be the question with which bridegrooms quiz themselves before the altar.

In the few wild seconds it took Ozzie's body to propel him to the edge of the roof, his self-examination began to grow fuzzy. Gazing down at the street, he became confused as to the problem beneath the question: was it, is-it-me-who-called-Binder-a-bastard? or, is-it-me-prancing-around-on-the-roof? However, the scene below settled all, for there is an instant in any action when whether it is you or somebody else is academic. The thief crams the money in his pockets and scoots out the window. The bridegroom signs the hotel register for two. And the boy on the roof finds a streetful of people gaping at him, necks stretched backwards, faces up, as though he were the ceiling of the Hayden Planetarium. Suddenly you know it's you.

"Oscar! Oscar Freedman!" A voice rose from the center of the crowd, a voice that, could it have been seen, would have looked like the writing on scroll. "Oscar Freedman, get down from there. Immediately!" Rabbi Binder was pointing one arm stiffly up at him; and at the end of that arm, one finger aimed menacingly. It was the attitude of a dictator, but one — the eyes confessed all — whose personal valet had spit neatly in his face.

Ozzie didn't answer. Only for a blink's length did he look towards Rabbi Binder. Instead his eyes began to fit together the world beneath him, to sort out people from places, friends from enemies, participants from spectators. In little jagged starlike clusters his friends stood around Rabbi Binder, who was still pointing. The topmost point on a star compounded not of angels but of five adolescent boys was Itzie. What a world it was, with those stars below, Rabbi Binder below . . . Ozzie, who a moment earlier hadn't been able to control his own body, started to feel the meaning of the word control: he felt Peace and he felt Power.

"Oscar Freedman, I'll give you three to come down."

Few dictators give their subjects three to do anything; but, as always, Rabbi Binder only looked dictatorial.

"Are you ready, Oscar?"

Ozzie nodded his head yes, although he had no intention in the world — the lower one of the celestial one he'd just entered — of coming down even if Rabbi Binder should give him a million.

"All right then," said Rabbi Binder. He ran a hand through his black Samson hair as though it were the gesture prescribed for uttering the first digit. Then, with his other hand cutting a circle out of the small piece of sky around him, he spoke. "One!"

There was no thunder. On the contrary, at that moment, as though "one" was the cue for which he had been waiting, the world's least thunderous person appeared on the synagogue steps. He did not so much come out the synagogue door as lean out, onto the darkening air. He clutched at the doorknob with one hand and looked up at the roof.

"Oy!"

Yakov Blotnik's old mind hobbled slowly, as if on crutches, and though he couldn't decide precisely what the boy was doing on the roof, he knew it wasn't good — that is, it wasn't-good-for-the-Jews. For Yakov Blotnik life had fractionated itself simply: things were either good-for-the-Jews or no-good-for-the-Jews.

He smacked his free hand to his in-sucked cheek, gently. "Oy, Gut!" And then quick as he was able, he jacked down his head and surveyed the street. There was Rabbi Binder (like a man at an auction with only three dollars in his pocket, he had just delivered a shaky "Two!"); there were the students, and that was all. So far it-wasn't-so-bad-for-the-Jews. But the boy had to come down immediately, before anybody saw. The problem: how to get the boy off the roof?

Anybody who has ever had a cat on the roof knows how to get him down. You call the fire department. Or first you call the operator and you ask her for the fire department. And the next thing there is great jamming of brakes and clanging of bells and shouting of instructions. And then the cat is off the roof. You do the same thing to get a boy off the roof.

That is, you do the same thing if you are Yakov Blotnik and you once had a cat on the roof.

When the engines, all four of them, arrived, Rabbi Binder had four times given Ozzie the count of three. The big hook-and-ladder swung around the corner and one of the firemen leaped from it, plunging headlong towards the yellow fire hydrant in front of the synagogue. With a huge wrench he began to unscrew the top nozzle. Rabbi Binder raced over to him and pulled at his shoulder.

"There's no fire . . ."

The fireman mumbled back of his shoulder and, heatedly, continued working at the nozzle.

"But there's no fire, there's no fire . . . " Binder shouted. When the fireman mumbled again, the rabbi grasped his face with both his hands and pointed it up at the roof.

To Ozzie it looked as though Rabbi Binder was trying to tug

the fireman's head out of his body, like a cork from a bottle. He had to giggle at the picture they made: it was a family portrait — rabbi in black skullcap, fireman in red fire hat, and the little yellow hydrant squatting beside like a kid brother, bareheaded. From the edge of the roof Ozzie waved at the portrait, a one-handed, flapping, mocking wave; in doing it his right foot slipped from under him. Rabbi Binder covered his eyes with his hands.

Firemen work fast. Before Ozzie had even regained his balance, a big, round, yellowed net was being held on the synagogue lawn. The firemen who held it looked up at Ozzie with stern, feelingless faces.

One of the firemen turned his head towards Rabbi Binder. "What, is the kid nuts or something?"

Rabbi Binder unpeeled his hands from his eyes, slowly, painfully, as if they were tape. Then he checked: nothing on the sidewalk, no dents in the net.

"Is he gonna jump, or what?" the fireman shouted.

In a voice not at all like a statue, Rabbi Binder finally answered. "Yes, yes, I think so . . . He's been threatening to . . . "

Threatening to? Why, the reason he was on the roof, Ozzie remembered, was to get away; he hadn't even thought about jumping. He had just run to get away, and the truth was that he hadn't really headed for the roof as much as he'd been chased there.

"What's his name, the kid?"

"Freedman," Rabbi Binder answered. "Oscar Freedman."

The fireman looked up at Ozzie. "What is it with you, Oscar? You gonna jump, or what?"

Ozzie did not answer. Frankly, the question had just arisen.

"Look, Oscar, if you're gonna jump, jump — and if you're not gonna jump, don't jump. But don't waste our time, willya?"

Ozzie looked at the fireman and then at Rabbi Binder. He wanted to see Rabbi Binder cover his eyes one more time.

"I'm going to jump."

And then he scampered around the edge of the roof to the corner, where there was no net below, and he flapped his arms at his sides, swishing the air and smacking his palms to his trousers on the downbeat. He began screaming like some kind of engine, "Wheeeee . . . wheeeeee," and leaning way out over the edge with the upper half of his body. The firemen whipped around to cover the ground with the net. Rabbi Binder mumbled a few words to Somebody and covered his eyes. Everything happened quickly, jerkily, as in a silent movie. The crowd, which had arrived with the fire engines, gave out a long, Fourth-of-July fireworks oooh-aahhh. In the excitement no one had paid the crowd much heed, except, of course, Yakov Blotnik, who swung from the doorknob counting heads. "Fier und tsvansik . . . finf und tsvantsik . . . Oy, Gut!" It wasn't like this with the cat.

Rabbi Binder peeked through his fingers, checked the sidewalk and net. Empty. But there was Ozzie racing to the other corner. The firemen raced with him but were unable to keep up. Whenever Ozzie wanted to he might jump and splatter himself upon the sidewalk, and by the time the firemen scooted to the spot all they could do with their net would be to cover the mess.

"Wheeeee . . . wheeeee . . ."

"Hey, Oscar," the winded fireman yelled, "What the hell is this, a game or something?"

"Wheeeee . . . wheeeee . . ."

"Hey, Oscar —"

But he was off now to the other corner, flapping his wings fiercely. Rabbi Binder couldn't take it any longer — the fire engines from nowhere, the screaming suicidal boy, the net. He fell to his knees, exhausted, and with his hands curled together in front of his chest like a little dome, he pleaded, "Oscar, stop it, Oscar. Don't jump, Oscar. Please come down . . . Please don't jump."

And futher back in the crowd a single voice, a single young voice, shouted a lone word to the boy on the roof.

"Jump!"

It was Itzie. Ozzie momentarily stopped flapping.

"Go ahead, Ozz — jump!" Itzie broke off his point of the star and courageously, with the inspiration not of a wise-guy but of a disciple, stood alone. "Jump, Ozz, jump!"

Still on his knees, his hands still curled, Rabbi Binder twisted his body back. He looked at Itzie, then, agonizingly, back to Ozzie.

"OSCAR, DON'T JUMP! PLEASE, DON'T JUMP . . . please please . . ."

"Jump!" This time it wasn't Itzie but another point of the star. By the time Mrs. Freedman arrived to keep her four-thirty appointment with Rabbi Binder, the whole little upside down heaven was shouting and pleading for Ozzie to jump, and Rabbi Binder no longer was pleading with him not to jump, but was crying into the dome of his hands.

Understandably Mrs. Freedman couldn't figure out what her son was doing on the roof. So she asked.

"Ozzie, my Ozzie, what are you doing? My Ozzie, what is it?"

Ozzie stopped wheeeeing and slowed his arms down to a cruising flap, the kind birds use in soft winds, but he did not answer. He stood against the low, clouded, darkening sky — light clicked down swiftly now, as on a small gear — flapping softly and gazing down at the small bundle of a woman who was his mother.

"What are you doing, Ozzie?" She turned towards the kneeling Rabbi Binder and rushed so close that only a paper-thickness of dusk lay between her stomach and his shoulders.

"What is my baby doing?"

Rabbi Binder gaped up at her but he too was mute. All that moved was the dome of his hands; it shook back and forth like a weak pulse.

"Rabbi, get him down! He'll kill himself. Get him down, my only baby . . ."

"I can't," Rabbi Binder said, "I can't . . ." and he turned his handsome head towards the crowd of boys behind him. "It's them. Listen to them."

And for the first time Mrs. Freedman saw the crowd of boys, and she heard what they were yelling.

"He's doing it for them. He won't listen to me. It's them." Rabbi Binder spoke like one in a trance.

"For them?"

"Yes."

"Why for them?"

"They want him to . . ."

Mrs. Freedman raised her two arms upward as though she

were conducting the sky. "For them he's doing it!" And then in a gesture older than pyramids, older than prophets and floods, her arms came slapping down to her sides. "A martyr I have. Look!" She tilted her head to the roof. Ozzie was still flapping softly. "My martyr."

"Oscar, come down, *please*," Rabbi Binder groaned.

In a startlingly even voice Mrs. Freedman called to the boy on the roof. "Ozzie, come down, Ozzie. Don't be a martyr, my baby."

As though it were a litany, Rabbi Binder repeated her words. "Don't be a martyr, my baby. Don't be a martyr."

"Gawhead, Ozz — *be* a Martin!" It was Itzie. "Be a Martin, be a Martin," and all the voices joined in singing for Martindom, whatever *it* was. "Be a Martin, be a Martin . . ."

Somehow when you're on a roof the darker it gets the less you can hear. All Ozzie knew was that two groups wanted two new things: his friends were spirited and musical about what they wanted; his mother and the rabbi were even-toned, chanting, about what they didn't want. The rabbi's voice was without tears now and so was his mother's.

The big net stared up at Ozzie like a sightless eye. The big, clouded sky pushed down. From beneath it looked like a gray corrugated board. Suddenly, looking up into that unsympathetic sky, Ozzie realized all the strangeness of what these people, his friends, were asking: they wanted him to jump, to kill himself; they were singing about it now — it made them that happy. And there was an even greater strangeness: Rabbi Binder was on his knees, trembling. If there was a question to be asked now it was not "Is it me?" but rather "Is it us? . . . Is it us?"

Being on the roof, it turned out, was a serious thing. If he jumped would the singing become dancing? Would it? What would jumping stop? Yearningly, Ozzie wished he could rip open the sky, plunge his hands through, and pull out the sun; and on the sun, like a coin, would be stamped JUMP or DON'T JUMP.

Ozzie's knees rocked and sagged a little under him as though they were setting him for a dive. His arms tightened, stiffened, froze, from shoulders to fingernails. He felt as if each part of his body were going to vote as to whether he should kill himself or not — and each part as though it were independent of *him*.

The light took an unexpected click down and the new darkness, like a gag, hushed the friends singing for this and the mother and rabbi chanting for that.

Ozzie stopped counting votes, and in a curiously high voice, like one who wasn't prepared for speech, he spoke.

"Mamma?"

"Yes, Oscar."

"Mamma, get down on your knees, like Rabbi Binder."

"Oscar —"

"Get down on your knees," he said, "or I'll jump."

Ozzie heard a whimper, then a quick rustling, and when he looked down where his mother had stood he saw the top of a head and beneath that a circle of dress. She was kneeling beside Rabbi Binder.

He spoke again. "Everybody kneel." There was the sound of everybody kneeling.

Ozzie looked around. With one hand he pointed towards the synagogue entrance. "Make *him* kneel."

There was a noise, not of kneeling, but of body-and-cloth stretching. Ozzie could hear Rabbi Binder saying in a gruff whisper, ". . . or he'll *kill* himself," and when next he looked there was Yakov Blotnik off the doorknob and for the first time in his life upon his knees in the Gentile posture of prayer.

As for the firemen — it is not as difficult as one might imagine to hold a net taut while you are kneeling.

Ozzie looked around again; and then he called to Rabbi Binder.

"Rabbi?"

"Yes, Oscar."

"Rabbi Binder, do you believe in God?"

"Yes."

"Do you believe God can do Anything?" Ozzie leaned his head out into the darkness. "Anything?"

"Oscar, I think —"

"Tell me you believe God can do Anything."

There was a second's hesitation. Then: "God can do Anything."

"Tell me you believe God can make a child without intercourse."

"He can."

"Tell me!"

"God," Rabbi Binder admitted, "can make a child without intercourse."

"Mamma, you tell me."

"God can make a child without intercourse," his mother said.

"Make *him* tell me." There was no doubt who *him* was.

In a few moments Ozzie heard an old comical voice say something to the increasing darkness about God.

Next, Ozzie made everybody say it. And then he made them all say they believed in Jesus Christ — first one at a time, then all together.

When the catechizing was through it was the beginning of evening. From the street it sounded as if the boy on the roof might have sighed.

"Ozzie?" A woman's voice dared to speak. "You'll come down now?"

There was no answer, but the woman waited, and when a voice finally did speak it was thin and crying, and exhausted as that of an old man who has just finished pulling the bells.

"Mamma, don't you see — you shouldn't hit me. He shouldn't hit me. You shouldn't hit me about God, Mamma. You should never hit anybody about God —"

"Ozzie, please come down now."

"Promise me, promise me you'll never hit anybody about God."

He had asked only his mother, but for some reason everyone kneeling in the street promised he would never hit anybody about God.

Once again there was silence.

"I can come down now, Mamma," the boy on the roof finally said. He turned his head both ways as though checking the traffic lights. "Now I can come down . . ."

And he did, right into the center of the yellow net that glowed in the evening's edge like an overgrown halo.

New Testament Readings

Mark 12:28-34

Then one of the scribes approached him. He had been listening to the discussion, and noticing how well Jesus had answered them. He put this question to him: "What are we to consider the greatest commandment of all?"

"The first and most important one is this," Jesus replied. " 'Hear, O Israel: The Lord our God, the Lord is one; and thou shalt love the Lord thy God with all thy heart, and with all thy soul, and with all thy mind, and with all thy strength.' The second is this, 'Thou shalt love thy neighbor as thyself.' No other commandment is greater than these."

"I am well answered," replied the scribe. "You are absolutely right when you say that there is one God and no other God exists but him; and to love him with the whole of our hearts, the whole of our intelligence and the whole of our energy, and to love our neighbors as ourselves is infinitely more important than all these burnt offerings and sacrifices."

Then Jesus, noting the thoughtfulness of his reply, said to him, "You are not far from the kingdom of God!" After this nobody felt like asking him anymore questions.

Matthew 7:1-2

"Don't criticize people, and you will not be criticized. For you will be judged by the way you criticize others, and the measure you give will be the measure you receive."

John 15:9-15

"I have loved you just as the Father has loved me. You must go on living in my love. If you keep my commandments you will live in my love just as I have kept my Father's commandments and live in his love. I have told you this so that you can share my joy, and that your happiness may be complete. This is my commandment: That you love one another as I have loved you. There is no greater love than this—that a man should lay down his life for his friends. You are my friends if you do what I tell you to do. I shall not call you servants any longer, for a servant does not share his master's confidence. No, I call you friends, now, because I have told you everything that I have heard from the Father."

Matthew 25:31-46

"But when the Son of Man comes in his splendor with all his angels with him, then he will take his seat on his glorious throne. All the nations will be assembled before him and he will separate men from each other like a shepherd separating sheep from goats. He will place the sheep on his right hand and the goats on his left.

"Then the king will say to those on his right: 'Come, you who have won my Father's blessing! Take your inheritance — the kingdom reserved for you since the foundation of the world! For I was hungry and you gave me food. I was thirsty and you gave me a drink. I was lonely and you made me welcome. I was naked and you clothed me. I was ill and you came and looked after me. I was in prison and you came to see me there.'

"Then the true men will answer him: 'Lord, when did we see *you* hungry and give you food? When did we see you thirsty and give you something to drink? When did we see you lonely and make you welcome, or see you naked and clothe you, or see you ill or in prison and go to see you?'

"And the king will reply, 'I assure you that whatever you did for the humblest of my brothers you did for me.'

"Then he will say to those on his left: 'Out of my presence, cursed as you are, into the eternal fire prepared for the devil and his angels! For I was hungry and you gave me nothing to eat, I was thirsty and you gave me nothing to drink. I was lonely and you never made me welcome. When I was naked you did nothing to clothe me; when I was sick and in prison you never cared about me.'

"Then they too will answer him: 'Lord, when did we ever see you hungry, or thirsty, or lonely, or naked, or sick, or in prison, and fail to look after you?'

"Then the king will answer them with these words, 'I assure you that whatever you failed to do to the humblest of my brothers you failed to do to me.'

"And these will go off to eternal punishment, but the true men to eternal life."

PART II

THOMAS WOLFE

The Far And the Near

On the outskirts of a little town upon a rise of land that swept back from the railway there was a tidy little cottage of white boards, trimmed vividly with green blinds. To one side of the house there was a garden neatly patterned with plots of growing vegetables, and an arbor for the grapes which ripened late in August. Before the house there were three mighty oaks which sheltered it in their clean and massive shade in summer, and to the other side there was a border of gay flowers. The whole place had an air of tidiness, thrift, and modest comfort.

Every day, a few minutes after two o'clock in the afternoon, the limited express between the two cities passed this spot. At that moment the great train, having halted for a breathing space at the town nearby, was beginning to lengthen evenly into its stroke, but it had not yet reached the full drive of its terrific speed. It swung into view deliberately, swept past with a powerful swaying motion of the engine, a low smooth rumble of its heavy cars upon pressed steel, and then it vanished in the cut. For a moment the progress of the engine could be marked by heavy bellowing puffs of smoke that burst at spaced intervals above the edges of the meadow grass, and finally nothing could be heard but the solid clacking tempo of the wheels receding into the drowsy stillness of the afternoon.

Every day for more than twenty years, as the train approached this house, the engineer had blown on the whistle, and every day, as soon as she heard this signal, a woman had appeared on the back porch of the little house and waved to him. At first she had a small child clinging to her skirts, and now this child had grown to full womanhood, and every day she, too, came with her mother to the porch and waved.

The engineer had grown old and gray in service. He had driven his great train, loaded with its weight of lives, across the land ten thousand times. His own children had grown up and married, and four times he had seen before him on the tracks the ghastly dot of tragedy converging like a cannon ball to its eclipse of horror at the boiler head — a light spring wagon filled with children, with its clustered row of small stunned faces, a cheap automobile stalled upon the tracks, set with the wooden figures of people paralyzed with fear, a battered hobo walking by the rail, too deaf and old to hear the whistle's warning, and a form flung past his window with a scream — all this the man had seen and known. He had known all the grief, the joy, the peril, and the labor such a man could know; he had grown seamed and weathered in his loyal service, and now, schooled by the qualities of faith and courage and humbleness that attended his labor, he had grown old, and had the grandeur and the wisdom these men have.

But no matter what peril or tragedy he had known, the vision of the little house and the women waving to him with a brave free motion of the arm had become fixed in the mind of the engineer as something beautiful and enduring, something beyond all change and ruin, and something that would always be the same, no matter what mishap, grief, or error might break the iron schedule of his days.

The sight of the little house and of these two women gave him the most extraordinary happiness he had ever known. He had seen them in a thousand lights, a hundred weathers. He had seen them through the harsh bare light of wintry gray across the brown and frosted stubble of earth, and he had seen them again in the green luring sorcery of April.

He felt for them and for the little house in which they lived such tenderness as a man might feel for his own children, and at length the picture of their lives was carved so sharply in his heart that he felt that he knew their lives completely, to every hour and moment of the day, and he resolved that one day, when his years of service should be ended, he would go and find these people and speak at last with them whose lives had been so wrought into his own.

That day came. At last the engineer stepped from a train onto the station platform of the town where these two women lived. His years upon the rail had ended. He was a pensioned servant of his company, with no more work to do. The engineer walked slowly through the station and out into the streets of the town. Everything was as strange to him as if he had never seen this town before. As he walked on, his sense of bewilderment and confusion grew. Could this be the town he had passed ten thousand times? Were these the same houses he had seen so often from the high windows of his cab? It was all as unfamiliar, as disquieting as a city in a dream, and the perplexity of his spirit increased as he went on.

Presently the houses thinned into the straggling outposts of the town, and the street faded into a country road — the one on which the women lived. And the man plodded on slowly in the heat and dust. At length he stood before the house he sought. He knew at once that he had found the proper place. He saw the lordly oaks before the house, the flower beds, the garden, and the arbor, and farther off, the glint of rails.

Yes, this was the house he sought, the place he had passed so many times, the destination he had longed for with such happiness. But now that he had found it, now that he was here, why did his hand falter on the gate; why had the town, the road, the earth, the very entrance to this place he loved turned unfamiliar as the landscape of some ugly dream? Why did he now feel this sense of confusion, doubt, and hopelessness?

At length he entered by the gate, walked slowly up the path and in a moment more had mounted three short steps that led up to the porch, and was knocking at the door. Presently he heard steps in the hall, the door was opened, and a woman stood facing him.

And instantly, with a sense of bitter loss and grief, he was sorry he had come. He knew at once that the woman who stood there looking at him with a mistrustful eye was the same woman who had waved to him so many thousand times. But her face was harsh and pinched and meager; the flesh sagged wearily in sallow folds, and the small eyes peered at him with timid suspicion and uneasy doubt. All the brave freedom, the warmth, and the affection that he had read into her gesture, vanished in the moment that he saw her and heard her unfriendly tongue.

And now his own voice sounded unreal and ghastly to him as he tried to explain his presence, to tell her who he was and the reason he had come. But he faltered on, fighting stubbornly against the horror of regret, confusion, disbelief that surged up in his spirit, drowning all his former joy and making his act of hope and tenderness seem shameful to him.

At length the woman invited him almost unwillingly into the house, and called her daughter in a harsh shrill voice. Then, for a brief agony of time, the man sat in an ugly little parlor, and he tried to talk while the two women stared at him with a dull, bewildered hostility, a sullen, timorous restraint.

And finally, stammering a crude farewell, he departed. He walked away down the path and then along the road toward town, and suddenly he knew that he was an old man. His heart, which had been brave and confident when he looked along the familiar vista of the rails, was now sick with doubt and horror as it saw the strange and unsuspected visage of an earth which had always been within a stone's throw of him, and which he had never seen or known. And he knew that all the magic of that bright lost way, the vista of that shining line, the imagined corner of that small good universe of hope's desire, was gone forever, could never be got back again.

FLANNERY O'CONNOR

The River

The child stood glum and limp in the middle of the dark living room while his father pulled him into a plaid coat. His right arm was hung in the sleeve but the father buttoned the coat anyway and pushed him forward toward a pale spotted hand that stuck through the half-open door.

"He ain't fixed right," a loud voice said from the hall.

"Well then for Christ's sake fix him," the father muttered. "It's six o'clock in the morning." He was in his bathrobe and barefooted. When he got the child to the door and tried to shut it, he found her looming in it, a speckled skeleton in a long pea-green coat and felt helmet.

"And his and my carfare," she said. "It'll be twict we have to ride the car."

He went in the bedroom again to get the money and when he came back, she and the boy were both standing in the middle of the room. She was taking stock. "I couldn't smell those dead cigarette butts long if I was ever to come sit with you," she said, shaking him down in his coat.

"Here's the change," the father said. He went to the door and opened it wide and waited.

After she had counted the money she slipped it somewhere inside her coat and walked over to a watercolor hanging near the phonograph. "I know what time it is," she said, peering closely at the black lines crossing into broken planes of violent color. "I ought to. My shift goes on at 10 P.M. and don't get off till 5 and it takes me one hour to ride the Vine Street car."

"Oh, I see," he said. "Well, we'll expect him back tonight, about eight or nine?"

"Maybe later," she said. "We're going to the river to a healing. This particular preacher don't get around this way often. I wouldn't have paid for that," she said, nodding at the painting, "I would have drew it myself."

"All right, Mrs. Connin, we'll see you then," he said drumming on the door.

A toneless voice called from the bedroom, "Bring me an ice-pack."

"Too bad his mamma's sick," Mrs. Connin said. "What's her trouble?"

"We don't know," he muttered.

"We'll ask the preacher to pray for her. He's healed a lot of folks. The Reverend Bevel Summers. Maybe she ought to see him sometime."

"Maybe so," he said. "We'll see you tonight," and he disappeared into the bedroom and left them to go.

The little boy stared at her silently, his nose and eyes running. He was four or five. He had a long face and bulging chin and half-shut eyes set far apart. He seemed mute and patient, like an old sheep waiting to be let out.

"You'll like this preacher," she said. "The Reverend Bevel Summers. You ought to hear him sing."

The bedroom door opened suddenly and the father stuck his head out and said, "Good-by, old man. Have a good time."

"Good-by," the little boy said and jumped as if he had been shot.

Mrs. Connin gave the watercolor another look. Then they

went out into the hall and rang for the elevator. "I wouldn't have drew it," she said.

Outside the gray morning was blocked off on either side by the unlit empty buildings. "It's going to fair up later," she said, "but this is the last time we'll be able to have any preaching at the river this year. Wipe your nose, Sugar Boy."

He began rubbing his sleeve across it but she stopped him. "That ain't nice," she said. "Where's your handkerchief?"

He put his hands in his pockets and pretended to look for it while she waited. "Some people don't care how they send one off," she murmured to her reflection in the coffee shop window. "You pervide." She took a red and blue flowered handkerchief out of her pocket and stooped down and began to work on his nose. "Now blow," she said and he blew. "You can borry it. Put it in your pocket."

He folded it up and put it in his pocket carefully and they walked on to the corner and leaned against the side of a closed drugstore to wait for the car. Mrs. Connin turned up her coat collar so that it met her hat in the back. Her eyelids began to droop and she looked as if she might go to sleep against the wall. The little boy put a slight pressure on her hand.

"What's your name?" she asked in a drowsy voice. "I don't know but only your last name. I should have found out your first name."

His name was Harry Ashfield and he had never thought at any time before of changing it. "Bevel," he said.

Mrs. Connin raised herself from the wall. "Why ain't that a coincident!" she said. "I told you that's the name of this preacher!"

"Bevel," he repeated.

She stood looking down at him as if he had become a marvel to her. "I'll have to see you meet him today," she said. "He's no ordinary preacher. He's a healer. He couldn't do nothing for Mr. Connin though. Mr. Connin didn't have the faith but he said he would try anything once. He had this griping in his gut."

The trolley appeared as a yellow spot at the end of the deserted street.

"He's gone to the government hospital now," she said, "and they taken one-third of his stomach. I tell him he better thank Jesus for what he's got left but he says he ain't thanking nobody. Well I declare," she murmured, "Bevel!"

They walked out to the tracks to wait. "Will he heal me?" Bevel asked.

"What you got?"

"I'm hungry," he decided finally.

"Didn't you have your breakfast?"

"I didn't have time to be hungry yet then," he said.

"Well when we get home we'll both have us something," she said. "I'm ready myself."

They got in the car and sat down a few seats behind the driver and Mrs. Connin took Bevel on her knees. "Now you be a good boy," she said, "and let me get some sleep. Just don't get off my lap." She lay her head back and as he watched, gradually her eyes closed and her mouth fell open to show a few long scattered teeth, some gold and some darker than her face: she began to whistle and blow like a musical skeleton. There was no one in the car but themselves and the driver and when he saw she was asleep, he took out the flowered handkerchief and unfolded it and examined it carefully. Then he folded it up again and unzipped a place in the innerlining of his coat and hid it in there and shortly he went to sleep himself.

Her house was a half-mile from the end of the car line, set back a little from the road. It was tan paper brick with a porch across the front of it and a tin top. On the porch there were three little boys of different sizes with identical speckled faces and one tall girl who had her hair up in so many aluminum curlers that it glared like the roof. The three boys followed them inside and closed in on Bevel. They looked at him silently, not smiling.

"That's Bevel," Mrs. Connin said, taking off her coat. "It's a coincident he's named the same as the preacher. These boys are J. C., Spivey, and Sinclair, and that's Sarah Mildred on the porch. Take off that coat and hang it on the bed post, Bevel."

The three boys watched him while he unbuttoned the coat and

took it off. Then they watched him hang it on the bed post and then they stood, watching the coat. They turned abruptly and went out the door and had a conference on the porch.

Bevel stood looking around him at the room. It was part kitchen and part bedroom. The entire house was two rooms and two porches. Close to his foot the tail of a light-colored dog moved up and down between two floor boards as he scratched his back on the underside of the house. Bevel jumped on it but the hound was experienced and had already withdrawn when his feet hit the spot.

The walls were filled with pictures and calendars. There were two round photographs of an old man and woman with collapsed mouths and another picture of a man whose eyebrows dashed out of two bushes of hair and clashed in a heap on the bridge of his nose; the rest of his face stuck out like a bare cliff to fall from. "That's Mr. Connin," Mrs. Connin said, standing back from the stove for a second to admire the face with him, "but it don't favor him any more." Bevel turned from Mr. Connin to a colored picture over the bed of a man wearing a white sheet. He had long hair and a gold circle around his head and he was sawing on a board while some children stood watching him. He was going to ask who that was when the three boys came in again and motioned for him to follow them. He thought of crawling under the bed and hanging onto one of the legs but the three boys only stood there, speckled and silent, waiting, and after a second he followed them at a little distance out on the porch and around the corner of the house. They started off through a field of rough yellow weeds to the hog pen, a five-foot boarded square full of shoats, which they intended to ease him over into. When they reached it, they turned and waited silently, leaning against the side.

He was coming very slowly, deliberately bumping his feet together as if he had trouble walking. Once he had been beaten up in the park by some strange boys when his sitter forgot him, but he hadn't known anything was going to happen that time until it was over. He began to smell a strong odor of garbage and to hear the noises of a wild animal. He stopped a few feet from the pen and waited, pale but dogged.

The three boys didn't move. Something seemed to have happened to them. They stared over his head as if they saw something coming behind him but he was afraid to turn his own head and look. Their speckles were pale and their eyes were still and gray as glass. Only their ears twitched slightly. Nothing happened. Finally, the one in the middle said, "She'd kill us," and turned, dejected and hacked, and climbed up on the pen and hung over, staring in.

Bevel sat down on the ground, dazed with relief, and grinned up at them.

The one sitting on the pen glanced at him severely. "Hey you," he said after a second, "if you can't climb up and see these pigs you can lift that bottom board off and look in thataway." He appeared to offer this as a kindness.

Bevel had never seen a real pig but he had seen a pig in a book and knew they were small fat pink animals with curly tails and round grinning faces and bow ties. He leaned forward and pulled eagerly at the board.

"Pull harder," the littlest boy said. "It's nice and rotten. Just lift out thet nail."

He eased a long reddish nail out of the soft wood.

"Now you can lift up the board and put your face to the . . ." a quiet voice began.

He had already done it and another face, gray, wet and sour, was pushing into his, knocking him down and back as it scraped out under the plank. Something snorted over him and charged back again, rolling him over and pushing him up from behind and then sending him forward, screaming through the yellow field, while it bounded behind.

The three Connins watched from where they were. The one sitting on the pen held the loose board back with his gangling foot. Their stern faces didn't brighten any but they seemed to become less taut, as if some great need had been partly satisfied. "Maw ain't going to like him lettin' out thet hawg," the smallest one said.

Mrs. Connin was on the back porch and caught Bevel up as he reached the steps. The hog ran under the house and subsided, panting, but the child screamed for five minutes. When she had finally calmed him down, she gave him his breakfast and let him sit on her lap while he ate it. The shoat climbed the two steps onto the back porch and stood outside the screen door, looking in with his head lowered sullenly. He was long-legged and hump-backed and part of one of his ears had been bitten off.

"Git away!" Mrs. Connin shouted. "That one yonder favors Mr. Paradise that has the gas station," she said. "You'll see him today at the healing. He's got the cancer over his ear. He always comes to show he ain't been healed."

The shoat stood squinting a few seconds longer and then moved off slowly. "I don't want to see him," Bevel said.

They walked to the river, Mrs. Connin in front with him and the three boys strung out behind and Sarah Mildred, the tall girl, at the end to holler if one of them ran out on the road. They looked like the skeleton of an old boat with two pointed ends, sailing slowly on the edge of the highway. The white Sunday sun followed at a little distance, climbing fast through a scum of gray cloud as if it meant to overtake them. Bevel walked on the outside edge, holding Mrs. Connin's hand and looking down into the orange and purple gulley that dropped off from the concrete.

It occurred to him that he was lucky this time that they had found Mrs. Connin who would take you away for the day instead of an ordinary sitter who only sat where you lived or went to the park. You found out more when you left where you lived. He had found out already this morning that he had been made by a carpenter named Jesus Christ. Before he had thought it had been a doctor named Sladewall, a fat man with a yellow mustache who gave him shots and thought his name was Herbert, but this must have been a joke. They joked a lot where he lived. If he had thought about it before, he would have thought Jesus Christ was a word like "oh" or "damn" or "God," or maybe somebody who had cheated them out of something sometime. When he had asked Mrs. Connin who the man in the sheet in the picture over her bed was, she had looked at him a while with her mouth open. Then she had said, "That's Jesus," and she had kept on looking at him.

In a few minutes she had got up and got a book out of the other room. "See here," she said, turning over the cover, "this belonged to my great grandmamma. I wouldn't part with it for nothing on earth." She ran her finger under some brown writing on a spotted page. "Emma Stevens Oakley, 1832," she said. "Ain't that something to have? And every word of it the gospel truth." She turned the next page and read him the name: "The Life of Jesus Christ for Readers Under Twelve." Then she read him the book.

It was a small book, pale brown on the outside with gold edges and a smell like old putty. It was full of pictures, one of the carpenter driving a crowd of pigs out of a man. They were real pigs, gray and sour-looking, and Mrs. Connin said Jesus had driven them all out of this one man. When she finished reading, she let him sit on the floor and look at the pictures again.

Just before they left for the healing, he had managed to get the book inside his innerlining without her seeing him. Now it made his coat hang down a little farther on one side than the other. His mind was dreamy and serene as they walked along and when they turned off the highway onto a long red clay road winding between banks of honeysuckle, he began to make wild leaps and pull forward on her hand as if he wanted to dash off and snatch the sun which was rolling away ahead of them now.

They walked on the dirt road for a while and then they crossed a field stippled with purple weeds and entered the shadows of a wood where the ground was covered with thick pine needles. He had never been in woods before and he walked carefully, looking from side to side as if he were entering a strange country. They moved along a bridle path that twisted downhill through crackling red leaves, and once, catching at a branch to keep himself from slipping, he looked into two frozen green-gold eyes enclosed in the darkness of a tree hole. At the bottom of the hill, the woods opened suddenly onto a pasture dotted here and there with black and white cows and sloping down, tier after tier, to a broad orange stream where the reflection of the sun was set like a diamond.

There were people standing on the near bank in a group,

singing. Long tables were set up behind them and a few cars and trucks were parked in a road that came up by the river. They crossed the pasture, hurrying, because Mrs. Connin, using her hand for a shed over her eyes, saw the preacher already standing out in the water. She dropped her basket on one of the tables and pushed the three boys in front of her into the knot of people so that they wouldn't linger by the food. She kept Bevel by the hand and eased her way up to the front.

The preacher was standing about ten feet out in the stream where the water came up to his knees. He was a tall youth in khaki trousers that he had rolled up higher than the water. He had on a blue shirt and a red scarf around his neck but no hat and his light-colored hair was cut in sideburns that curved into the hollows of his cheeks. His face was all bone and red light reflected from the river. He looked as if he might have been nineteen years old. He was singing in a high twangy voice, above the singing on the bank, and he kept his hands behind him and his head tilted back.

He ended the hymn on a high note and stood silent, looking down at the water and shifting his feet in it. Then he looked up at the people on the bank. They stood close together, waiting; their faces were solemn but expectant and every eye was on him. He shifted his feet again.

"Maybe I know why you come," he said in the twangy voice, "maybe I don't.

"If you ain't come for Jesus, you ain't come for me. If you just come to see can you leave your pain in the river, you ain't come for Jesus. You can't leave your pain in the river," he said. "I never told nobody that." He stopped and looked down at his knees.

"I seen you cure a woman oncet!" a sudden high voice shouted from the hump of people. "Seen that woman git up and walk out straight where she had limped in!"

The preacher lifted one foot and then the other. He seemed almost but not quite to smile. "You might as well go home if that's what you come for," he said.

Then he lifted his head and arms and shouted, "Listen to what I got to say, you people! There ain't but one river and that's the River of Life, made out of Jesus' Blood. That's the river you have to lay your pain in, in the River of Faith, in the River of Life, in the River of Love, in the rich red river of Jesus' Blood, you people!"

His voice grew soft and musical. "All the rivers come from that one River and go back to it like it was the ocean sea and if you believe, you can lay your pain in that River and get rid of it because that's the River that was made to carry sin. It's a River full of pain itself, pain itself, moving toward the Kingdom of Christ, to be washed away, slow, you people, slow as this here old red water river round my feet.

"Listen," he sang, "I read in Mark about an unclean man, I read in Luke about a blind man, I read in John about a dead man! Oh you people hear! The same blood that makes this River red, made that leper clean, made that blind man stare, made that dead man leap! You people with trouble," he cried, "lay it in that River of Blood, lay it in that River of Pain, and watch it move away toward the Kingdom of Christ."

While he preached, Bevel's eyes followed drowsily the slow circles of two silent birds revolving high in the air. Across the river there was a low red and gold grove of sassafras with hills of dark blue trees behind it and an occasional pine jutting over the skyline. Behind, in the distance, the city rose like a cluster of warts on the side of the mountain. The birds revolved downward and dropped lightly in the top of the highest pine and sat hunch-shouldered as if they were supporting the sky.

"If it's this River of Life you want to lay your pain in, then come up," the preacher said, "and lay your sorrow here. But don't be thinking this is the last of it because this old red river don't end here. This old red suffering stream goes on, you people, slow to the Kingdom of Christ. This old red river is good to Baptize in, good to lay your faith in, good to lay your pain in, but it ain't this muddy water here that saves you. I been all up and down this river this week," he said. "Tuesday I was in Fortune Lake, next day in Ideal, Friday me and my wife drove to Lulawillow to see a sick man there. Them people didn't see no healing," he said and his face burned redder for a second. "I never said they would."

While he was talking a fluttering figure had begun to move forward with a kind of butterfly movement — an old woman with flapping arms whose head wobbled as if it might fall off any second. She managed to lower herself at the edge of the bank and let her arms churn in the water. Then she bent farther and pushed her face down in it and raised herself up finally, streaming wet; and still flapping, she turned a time or two in a blind circle until someone reached out and pulled her back into the group.

"She's been that way for thirteen years," a rough voice shouted. "Pass the hat and give this kid his money. That's what he's here for." The shout, directed out to the boy in the river, came from a huge old man who sat like a humped stone on the bumper of a long ancient gray automobile. He had on a gray hat that was turned down over one ear and up over the other to expose a purple bulge on his left temple. He sat bent forward with his hands hanging between his knees and his small eyes half closed.

Bevel stared at him once and then moved into the folds of Mrs. Connin's coat and hid himself.

The boy in the river glanced at the old man quickly and raised his fist. "Believe Jesus or the devil!" he cried. "Testify to one or the other!"

"I know from my self-experience," a woman's mysterious voice called from the knot of people, "I know from it that this preacher can heal. My eyes have been opened! I testify to Jesus!"

The preacher lifted his arms quickly and began to repeat all that he had said before about the River and the Kingdom of Christ and the old man sat on the bumper, fixing him with a narrow squint. From time to time Bevel stared at him again from around Mrs. Connin.

A man in overalls and a brown coat leaned forward and dipped his hand in the water quickly and shook it and leaned back, and a woman held a baby over the edge of the bank and splashed its feet with water. One man moved a little distance away and sat down on the bank and took off his shoes and waded out into the stream; he stood there for a few minutes with his face tilted as far back as it would go, then he waded back and put on his shoes. All this time, the preacher sang and did not appear to watch what went on.

As soon as he stopped singing, Mrs. Connin lifted Bevel up and said, "Listen here, preacher, I got a boy from town today that I'm keeping. His mamma's sick and he wants you to pray for her. And this is a coincident — his name is Bevel! Bevel," she said, turning to look at the people behind her, "same as his. Ain't that a coincident, though?"

There were some murmurs and Bevel turned and grinned over her shoulder at the faces looking at him. "Bevel," he said in a loud jaunty voice.

"Listen," Mrs. Connin said, "have you ever been Baptized, Bevel?"

He only grinned.

"I suspect he ain't ever been Baptized," Mrs. Connin said, raising her eyebrows at the preacher.

"Swang him over here," the preacher said and took a stride forward and caught him.

He held him in the crook of his arm and looked at the grinning face. Bevel rolled his eyes in a comical way and thrust his face forward, close to the preacher's. "My name is Bevvvuuuuul," he said in a loud deep voice and let the tip of his tongue slide across his mouth.

The preacher didn't smile. His bony face was rigid and his narrow gray eyes reflected the almost colorless sky. There was a loud laugh from the old man sitting on the car bumper and Bevel grasped the back of the preacher's collar and held it tightly. The grin had already disappeared from his face. He had the sudden feeling that this was not a joke. Where he lived everything was a joke. From the preacher's face, he knew immediately that nothing the preacher said or did was a joke. "My mother named me that," he said quickly.

"Have you ever been Baptized?" the preacher asked.

"What's that?" he murmured.

"If I Baptize you," the preacher said, "you'll be able to go to the Kingdom of Christ. You'll be washed in the river of suffering, son, and you'll go by the deep river of life. Do you want that?"

"Yes," the child said, and thought, I won't go back to the apartment then, I'll go under the river.

"You won't be the same again," the preacher said. "You'll count." Then he turned his face to the people and began to preach and Bevel looked over his shoulder at the pieces of the white sun scattered in the river. Suddenly the preacher said, "All right, I'm going to Baptize you now," and without more warning, he tightened his hold and swung him upside down and plunged his head into the water. He held him under while he said the words of Baptism and then he jerked him up again and looked sternly at the gasping child. Bevel's eyes were dark and dilated. "You count now," the preacher said. "You didn't even count before."

The little boy was too shocked to cry. He spit out the muddy water and rubbed his wet sleeve into his eyes and over his face.

"Don't forget his mamma," Mrs. Connin called. "He wants you to pray for his mamma. She's sick."

"Lord," the preacher said, "we pray for somebody in affliction who isn't here to testify. Is your mother sick in the hospital?" he asked. "Is she in pain?"

The child stared at him. "She hasn't got up yet," he said in a high dazed voice. "She has a hangover." The air was so quiet he could hear the broken pieces of the sun knocking the water.

The preacher looked angry and startled. The red drained out of his face and the sky appeared to darken in his eyes. There was a loud guffaw from the bank and Mr. Paradise shouted, "Haw! Cure the afflicted woman with the hangover!" and began to beat his knee with his fist.

"He's had a long day," Mrs. Connin said, standing with him in the door of the apartment and looking sharply into the room where the party was going on. "I reckon it's past his regular bedtime." One of Bevel's eyes was closed and the other half closed; his nose was running and he kept his mouth open and breathed through it. The damp plain coat dragged down on one side.

That would be her, Mrs. Connin decided, in the black britches — long black satin britches and barefoot sandals and red toenails. She was lying on half the sofa, with her knees crossed in the air and her head propped on the arm. She didn't get up.

"Hello, Harry," she said. "Did you have a big day?" She had a long pale face, smooth and blank, and straight sweet-potato-colored hair, pulled back.

The father went off to get the money. There were two other couples. One of the men, blond with little violet-blue eyes, leaned out of his chair and said, "Well Harry, old man, have a big day?"

"His name ain't Harry. It's Bevel," Mrs. Connin said.

"His name is Harry," *she* said from the sofa. "Whoever heard of anybody named Bevel?"

The little boy had seemed to be going to sleep on his feet, his head drooping farther and farther forward; he pulled it back suddenly and opened one eye; the other was stuck.

"He told me this morning his name was Bevel," Mrs. Connin said in a shocked voice. "The same as our preacher. We been all day at a preaching and healing at the river. He said his name was Bevel, the same as the preacher's. That's what he told me."

"Bevel!" his mother said. "My God! what a name."

"This preacher is named Bevel and there's no better preacher around," Mrs. Connin said. "And furthermore," she added in a defiant tone, "he Baptized this child this morning!"

His mother sat straight up. "Well the nerve!" she muttered.

"Furthermore," Mrs. Connin said, "he's a healer and he prayed for you to be healed."

"Healed!" she almost shouted. "Healed of what for Christ's sake?"

"Of your affliction," Mrs. Connin said icily.

The father had returned with the money and was standing near Mrs. Connin waiting to give it to her. His eyes were lined with red threads. "Go on, go on," he said, "I want to hear more about her affliction. The exact nature of it has escaped . . ." He waved the bill and his voice trailed off. "Healing by prayer is mighty inexpensive," he murmured.

Mrs. Connin stood a second, staring into the room, with a skeleton's appearance of seeing everything. Then, without taking the money, she turned and shut the door behind her. The father swung around, smiling vaguely, and shrugged. The rest of them were looking at Harry. The little boy began to shamble toward the bedroom.

"Come here, Harry," his mother said. He automatically shifted his direction toward her without opening his eyes any farther. "Tell me what happened today," she said when he reached her. She began to pull off his coat.

"I don't know," he muttered.

"Yes you do know," she said, feeling the coat heavier on one side. She unzipped the innerlining and caught the book and a dirty handkerchief as they fell out. "Where did you get these?"

"I don't know," he said and grabbed for them. "They're mine. She gave them to me."

She threw the handkerchief down and held the book too high for him to reach and began to read it, her face after a second assuming an exaggerated comical expression. The others moved around and looked at it over her shoulder. "My God," somebody said.

One of the men peered at it sharply from behind a thick pair of glasses. "That's valuable," he said. "That's a collector's item," and he took it away from the rest of them and retired to another chair.

"Don't let George go off with that," his girl said.

"I tell you it's valuable," George said. "1832."

Bevel shifted his direction again toward the room where he slept. He shut the door behind him and moved slowly in the darkness to the bed and sat down and took off his shoes and got under the cover. After a minute a shaft of light let in the tall silhouette of his mother. She tiptoed lightly across the room and sat down on the edge of his bed. "What did that dolt of a preacher say about me?" she whispered. "What lies have you been telling today, honey?"

He shut his eye and heard her voice from a long way away, as if he were under the river, and she on top of it. She shook his shoulder. "Harry," she said, leaning down and putting her mouth to his ear, "tell me what he said." She pulled him into a sitting position and he felt as if he had been drawn up from under the river. "Tell me," she whispered and her bitter breath covered his face.

He saw the pale oval close to him in the dark. "He said I'm not the same now," he muttered. "I count."

After a second, she lowered him by his shirt front onto the pillow. She hung over him an instant and brushed her lips against his forehead. Then she got up and moved away, swaying her hips lightly through the shaft of light.

He didn't wake up early but the apartment was still dark and close when he did. For a while he lay there, picking his nose and eyes. Then he sat up in bed and looked out the window. The sun came in palely, stained gray by the glass. Across the street at the Empire Hotel, a colored cleaning woman was looking down from an upper window, resting her face on her folded arms. He got up and put on his shoes and went to the bathroom and then into the front room. He ate two crackers spread with anchovy paste, that he found on the coffee table, and drank some ginger ale left in a bottle and looked around for his book but it was not there.

The apartment was silent except for the faint humming of the refrigerator. He went into the kitchen and found some raisin bread heels and spread a half jar of peanut butter between them and climbed up on the tall kitchen stool and sat chewing the sandwich slowly, wiping his nose every now and then on his shoulder. When he finished he found some chocolate milk and drank that. He would rather have had the ginger ale he saw but they left the bottle openers where he couldn't reach them. He studied what was left in the refrigerator for a while — some shriveled vegetables that she had forgot were there and a lot of brown oranges that she bought and didn't squeeze; there were three or four kinds of cheese and something fishy in a paper bag; the rest was a pork bone. He left the refrigerator door open and wandered back into the dark living room and sat down on the sofa.

He decided they would be out cold until one o'clock and that they would all have to go to a restaurant for lunch. He wasn't high enough for the table yet and the waiter would bring a highchair and he was too big for a highchair. He sat in the middle of the sofa, kicking it with his heels. Then he got up and wandered around the room, looking into the ashtrays at the butts as if this might be a habit. In his own room he had picture books and blocks but they were for the most part torn up; he found the way to get new ones was to tear up the ones he had. There was very little to do at any time but eat; however, he was not a fat boy.

He decided he would empty a few of the ashtrays on the floor. If he only emptied a few, she would think they had fallen. He emptied two, rubbing the ashes carefully into the rug with his finger. Then he lay on the floor for a while, studying his feet which he held up in the air. His shoes were still damp and he began to think about the river.

Very slowly, his expression changed as if he were gradually seeing appear what he didn't know he'd been looking for. Then all of a sudden he knew what he wanted to do.

He got up and tiptoed into their bedroom and stood in the dim light there, looking for her pocketbook. His glance passed her long pale arm hanging off the edge of the bed down to the floor, and across the white mound his father made, and past the crowded bureau, until it rested on the pocketbook hung on the back of a chair. He took a car-token out of it and half a package of Life Savers. Then he left the apartment and caught the car at the corner. He hadn't taken a suitcase because there was nothing from there he wanted to keep.

He got off the car at the end of the line and started down the road he and Mrs. Connin had taken the day before. He knew there wouldn't be anybody at her house because the three boys and the girl went to school and Mrs. Connin had told him she went out to clean. He passed her yard and walked on the way they had gone to the river. The paper brick houses were far apart and after a while the dirt place to walk on ended and he had to walk on the edge of the highway. The sun was pale yellow and high and hot.

He passed a shack with an orange gas pump in front of it but he didn't see the old man looking out at nothing in particular from the doorway. Mr. Paradise was having an orange drink. He finished it slowly, squinting over the bottle at the small plaid-coated figure disappearing down the road. Then he set the empty bottle on a bench and, still squinting, wiped his sleeve over his mouth. He went in the shack and picked out a peppermint stick, a foot long and two inches thick, from the candy shelf, and stuck it in his hip pocket. Then he got in his car and drove slowly down the highway after the boy.

By the time Bevel came to the field speckled with purple weeds, he was dusty and sweating and he crossed it at a trot to get into the woods as fast as he could. Once inside, he wandered from tree to tree, trying to find the path they had taken yesterday. Finally he found a line worn in the pine needles and followed it until he saw the steep trail twisting down through the trees.

Mr. Paradise had left his automobile back some way on the road and had walked to the place where he was accustomed to sit almost every day, holding an unbaited fishline in the water while he stared at the river passing in front of him. Anyone looking at him from a distance would have seen an old boulder half hidden in the bushes.

Bevel didn't see him at all. He only saw the river, shimmering reddish yellow, and bounded into it with his shoes and his coat on and took a gulp. He swallowed some and spit the rest out and then he stood there in water up to his chest and looked around him. The sky was a clear pale blue, all in one piece — except for the hole the sun made — and fringed around the bottom with treetops. His coat floated to the surface and surrounded him like a strange gay lily pad and he stood grinning in the sun. He intended not to fool with preachers any more but to Baptize himself and to keep on going this time until he found the Kingdom of Christ in the river. He didn't mean to waste any more time. He put his head under the water at once and pushed forward.

In a second he began to gasp and sputter and his head reappeared on the surface; he started under again and the same thing happened. The river wouldn't have him. He tried again and came up, choking. This was the way it had been when the preacher held him under — he had had to fight with something that pushed him back in the face. He stopped and thought suddenly: it's another joke, it's just another joke! He thought how far he had come for nothing and he began to hit and splash and kick the filthy river. His feet were already treading on nothing. He gave one low cry of pain and indignation. Then he heard a shout and turned his head and saw something like a giant pig bounding after him, shaking a red and white club and shouting. He plunged under once and this time the waiting current caught him like a long gentle hand and pulled him swiftly forward and down. For an instant he was overcome with surprise; then since he was moving quickly and knew that he was getting somewhere, all his fury and fear left him.

Mr. Paradise's head appeared from time to time on the surface of the water. Finally, far downstream, the old man rose like some ancient water monster and stood empty-handed, staring with his dull eyes as far down the river line as he could see.

SHIRLEY JACKSON

The Lottery

The morning of June 27th was clear and sunny, with the fresh warmth of a full-summer day; the flowers were blossoming profusely and the grass was richly green. The people of the village began to gather in the square, between the post office and the bank, around ten o'clock; in some towns there were so many people that the lottery took two days and had to be started on June 26th, but in this village, where there were only about three hundred people, the whole lottery took less than two hours, so it could begin at ten o'clock in the morning and still be through in time to allow the villagers to get home for noon dinner.

The children assembled first, of course. School was recently over for the summer, and the feeling of liberty sat uneasily on most of them; they tended to gather together quietly for a while before they broke into boisterous play, and their talk was still of the classroom and the teacher, of books and reprimands. Bobby Martin had already stuffed his pockets full of stones, and the other boys soon followed his example, selecting the smoothest and roundest stones; Bobby and Harry Jones and Dickie Delacroix — the villagers pronounced this name "Dellacroy" — eventually made a great pile of stones in one corner of the square and guarded it against the raids of the other boys. The girls stood aside, talking among themselves, looking over their shoulders at the boys, and the very small children rolled in the dust or clung to the hands of their older brothers or sisters.

Soon the men began to gather, surveying their own children, speaking of planting and rain, tractors and taxes. They stood together, away from the pile of stones in the corner, and their jokes were quiet and they smiled rather than laughed. The women, wearing faded house dresses and sweaters, came shortly after their menfolk. They greeted one another and exchanged bits of gossip as they went to join their husbands. Soon the women, standing by their husbands, began to call to their children, and the children came reluctantly, having to be called four or five times. Bobby Martin ducked under his mother's grasping hand and ran, laughing, back to the pile of stones. His father spoke up sharply, and Bobby came quickly and took his place between his father and his oldest brother.

The lottery was conducted — as were the square dances, the teen-age club, the Halloween program — by Mr. Summers, who had time and energy to devote to civic activities. He was a round-faced, jovial man and he ran the coal business, and people were sorry for him, because he had no children and his wife was a scold. When he arrived in the square, carrying the black wooden box, there was a murmur of conversation among the villagers, and he waved and called, "Little late today, folks." The postmaster, Mr. Graves, followed him, carrying a three-legged stool, and the stool was put in the center of the square and Mr. Summers set the black box down on it. The villagers kept their distance, leaving a space between themselves and the stool, and when Mr. Summers said, "Some of you fellows want to give me a hand?" there was a hesitation before two men, Mr. Martin and his oldest son, Baxter, came forward to hold the box steady on the stool while Mr. Summers stirred up the papers inside it.

The original paraphernalia for the lottery had been lost long ago, and the black box now resting on the stool had been put into use even before Old Man Warner, the oldest man in town, was born. Mr. Summers spoke frequently to the villagers about making a new box, but no one liked to upset even as much tradition as was represented by the black box. There was a story that the present box had been made with some pieces of the box that had preceded it, the one that had been constructed when the first people settled down to make a village here. Every year, after the lottery, Mr. Summers began talking again about a new box, but every year the subject was allowed to fade off without anything's being done. The black box grew shabbier each year; by now it was no longer completely black but splintered badly along one side to show the original wood color, and in some places faded or stained.

Mr. Martin and his oldest son, Baxter, held the black box securely on the stool until Mr. Summers had stirred the papers thoroughly with his hand. Because so much of the ritual had been forgotten or discarded, Mr. Summers had been successful in having slips of papers substituted for the chips of wood that had been used for generations. Chips of wood, Mr. Summers had argued had been all very well when the village was tiny but now that the population was more than three hundred and likely to keep on growing, it was necessary to use something that would fit more easily into the black box. The night before the lottery, Mr. Summers and Mr. Graves made up the slips of paper and put them in the box, and it was then taken to the safe of Mr. Summers' coal company and locked up until Mr. Summers was ready to take it to the square next morning. The rest of the year, the box was put away, sometimes one place, sometimes another; it had spent one year in Mr. Graves's barn and another year underfoot in the post office, and sometimes it was set on a shelf in the Martin grocery and left there.

There was a great deal of fussing to be done before Mr. Summers declared the lottery open. There were the lists to make up — of heads of families, heads of households in each family, members of each household in each family. There was the proper swearing-in of Mr. Summers by the postmaster, as the official of the lottery; at one time, some people remembered, there had been a recital of some sort, performed by the official of the lottery, a perfunctory, tuneless chant that had been rattled off duly each year; some people believed that the official of the lottery used to stand just so when he said or sang it, others believed that he was supposed to walk among the people, but years and years ago this part of the ritual had been allowed to lapse. There had been, also, a ritual salute, which the official of the lottery had had to use in addressing each person who came up to draw from the box, but this also had changed with time, until now it was felt necessary only for the official to speak to each person approaching. Mr. Summers was very good at all this; in his clean white shirt and blue jeans, with one hand resting carelessly on the black box, he seemed very proper and important as he talked interminably to Mr. Graves and the Martins.

Just as Mr. Summers finally left off talking and turned to the assembled villagers, Mrs. Hutchinson came hurriedly along the path to the square, her sweater thrown over her shoulders, and slid into place in the back of the crowd. "Clean forgot what day it was," she said to Mrs. Delacroix, who stood next to her, and they both laughed softly. "Thought my old man was out back stacking wood," Mrs. Hutchinson went on, "and then I looked out the window and the kids were gone, and then I remembered it was the twenty-seventh and came a-running." She dried her hands on her apron, and Mrs. Delacroix said, "You're in time, though. They're still talking away up there."

Mrs. Hutchinson craned her neck to see through the crowd and found her husband and children standing near the front. She tapped Mrs. Delacroix on the arm as a farewell and began to make her way through the crowd. The people separated good-humoredly to let her through; two or three people said, in voices just loud enough to be heard across the crowd, "Here comes your Missus, Hutchinson," and "Bill, she made it after all." Mrs. Hutchinson reached her husband, and Mr. Summers, who had been waiting, said cheerfully, "Thought we were going to have to go on without you, Tessie." Mrs. Hutchinson said, grinning, "Wouldn't have me leave m'dishes in the sink, now, would you, Joe?," and soft laughter ran through the crowd as the people stirred back into position after Mrs. Hutchinson's arrival.

"Well, now," Mr. Summers said soberly, "guess we better get

started, get this over with, so's we can go back to work. Anybody ain't here?"

"Dunbar," several people said. "Dunbar, Dunbar."

Mr. Summers consulted his list. "Clyde Dunbar," he said. "That's right. He's broke his leg, hasn't he? Who's drawing for him?"

"Me, I guess," a woman said, and Mr. Summers turned to look at her. "Wife draws for her husband," Mr. Summers said. "Don't you have a grown boy to do it for you, Janey?" Although Mr. Summers and everyone else in the village knew the answer perfectly well, it was the business of the official of the lottery to ask such questions formally. Mr. Summers waited with an expression of polite interest while Mrs. Dunbar answered.

"Horace's not but sixteen yet," Mrs. Dunbar said regretfully. "Guess I gotta fill in for the old man this year."

"Right," Mr. Summers said. He made a note on the list he was holding. Then he asked, "Watson boy drawing this year?"

A tall boy in the crowd raised his hand. "Here," he said. "I'm drawing for m'mother and me." He blinked his eyes nervously and ducked his head as several voices in the crowd said things like "Good fellow, Jack," and "Glad to see your mother's got a man to do it."

"Well," Mr. Summers said, "guess that's everyone. Old Man Warner make it?"

"Here," a voice said, and Mr. Summers nodded.

A sudden hush fell on the crowd as Mr. Summers cleared his throat and looked at the list. "All ready?" he called. "Now, I'll read the names — heads of families first — and the men come up and take a paper out of the box. Keep the paper folded in your hand without looking at it until everyone has had a turn. Everything clear?

The people had done it so many times that they only half listened to the directions; most of them were quiet, wetting their lips, not looking around. Then Mr. Summers raised one hand high and said, "Adams." A man disengaged himself from the crowd and came forward. "Hi, Steve," Mr. Summers said, and Mr. Adams said, "Hi, Joe." They grinned at one another humorlessly and nervously. Then Mr. Adams reached into the black box and took out a folded paper. He held it firmly by one corner as he turned and went hastily back to his place in the crowd, where he stood a little apart from his family, not looking down at his hand.

"Allen," Mr. Summers said. "Andrews. . . . Bentham."

"Seems like there's no time at all between lotteries any more," Mrs. Delacroix said to Mrs. Graves in the back row. "Seems like we got through with the last one only last week."

"Time sure goes fast," Mrs. Graves said.

"Clark. . . . Delacroix."

"There goes my old man," Mrs. Delacroix said. She held her breath while her husband went forward.

"Dunbar," Mr. Summers said, and Mrs. Dunbar went steadily to the box while one of the women said, "Go on, Janey," and another said, "There she goes."

"We're next," Mrs. Graves said. She watched while Mr. Graves came around from the side of the box, greeted Mr. Summers gravely, and selected a slip of paper from the box. By now, all through the crowd there were men holding the small folded papers in their large hands, turning them over and over nervously. Mrs. Dunbar and her two sons stood together, Mrs. Dunbar holding the slip of paper.

"Harburt. . . . Hutchinson."

"Get up there, Bill," Mrs. Hutchinson said, and the people near her laughed.

"Jones."

"They do say," Mr. Adams said to Old Man Warner, who stood next to him, "that over in the north village they're talking of giving up the lottery."

Old Man Warner snorted. "Pack of crazy fools," he said "Listening to the young folks, nothing's good enough for *them.* Next thing you know, they'll be wanting to go back to living in caves, nobody work any more, live *that* way for a while. Used to be a saying about 'Lottery in June, corn be heavy soon.' First thing you know, we'd be eating stewed chickweed and acorns. There's *always* been a lottery," he added petulantly. "Bad enough to see young Joe Summers up there joking with everybody."

"Some places have already quit lotteries," Mrs. Adams said.

"Nothing but trouble in *that*," Old Man Warner said stoutly. "Pack of young fools."

"Martin." And Bobby Martin watched his father go forward. "Overdyke. . . . Percy."

"I wish they'd hurry," Mrs. Dunbar said to her older son. "I wish they'd hurry."

"They're almost through," her son said.

"You get ready to run tell Dad," Mrs. Dunbar said.

Mr. Summers called his own name and then stepped forward precisely and selected a slip from the box. Then he called, "Warner."

"Seventy-seventh year I been in the lottery," Old Man Warner said as he went through the crowd. "Seventy-seventh time."

"Watson." The tall boy came awkwardly through the crowd. Someone said, "Don't be nervous, Jack," and Mr. Summers said, "Take your time, son."

"Zanini."

After that, there was a long pause, a breathless pause, until Mr. Summers, holding his slip of paper in the air, said, "All right, fellows." For a minute no one moved, and then all the slips of paper were opened. Suddenly, all women began to speak at once, saying, "Who is it?" "Who's got it?" "Is it the Dunbars?" "Is it the Watsons?" Then the voices began to say, "It's Hutchinson. It's Bill." "Bill Hutchinson got it."

"Go tell your father," Mrs. Dunbar said to her older son.

People began to look around to see the Hutchinsons. Bill Hutchinson was standing quiet, staring down at the paper in his hand. Suddenly, Tessie Hutchinson shouted to Mr. Summers, "You didn't give him time enough to take any paper he wanted. I saw you. It wasn't fair."

"Be a good sport, Tessie," Mrs. Delacroix called, and Mrs. Graves said, "All of us took the same chance."

"Shut up, Tessie," Bill Hutchinson said.

"Well, everyone," Mr. Summers said, "that was done pretty

fast, and now we've got to be hurrying a little more to get done in time." He consulted his next list. "Bill," he said, "you draw for the Hutchinson family. You got any other households in the Hutchinsons?"

"There's Don and Eva," Mrs. Hutchinson yelled. "Make *them* take their chance!"

"Daughters draw with their husbands' families, Tessie," Mr. Summers said gently. "You know that as well as anyone else."

"It wasn't *fair*," Tessie said.

"I guess not, Joe," Bill Hutchinson said regretfully. "My daughter draws with her husband's family, that's only fair. And I've got no other family except the kids."

"Then as far as drawing for families is concerned, it's you," Mr. Summers said in explanation, "and as far as drawing for households is concerned, that's you, too. Right?"

"Right," Bill Hutchinson said.

"How many kids, Bill?" Mr. Summers asked formally.

"Three," Bill Hutchinson said. "There's Bill, Jr., and Nancy, and little Dave. And Tessie and me."

"All right, then," Mr. Summers said. "Harry, you got their tickets back?"

Mr. Graves nodded and held up the slips of paper. "Put them in the box, then," Mr. Summers directed. "Take Bill's and put it in."

"I think we ought to start over," Mrs. Hutchinson said, as quietly as she could. "I tell you it wasn't *fair*. You didn't give him time enough to choose. *Every*body saw that."

Mr. Graves had selected the five slips and put them in the box, and he dropped all the papers but those onto the ground, where the breeze caught them and lifted them off.

"Listen, everybody," Mrs. Hutchinson was saying to the people around her.

"Ready, Bill?" Mr. Summers asked, and Bill Hutchinson, with one quick glance around at his wife and children, nodded.

"Remember," Mr. Summers said, "take the slips and keep them folded until each person has taken one. Harry, you help little

Dave." Mr. Graves took the hand of the little boy, who came willingly with him up to the box. "Take a paper out of the box, Davy," Mr. Summers said. Davy put his hand into the box and laughed. "Take just *one* paper," Mr. Summers said. "Harry, you hold it for him." Mr. Graves took the child's hand and removed the folded paper from the tight fist and held it while little Dave stood next to him and looked up at him wonderingly.

"Nancy next," Mr. Summers said. Nancy was twelve, and her school friends breathed heavily as she went forward, switching her skirt, and took a slip daintily from the box. "Bill, Jr.," Mr. Summers said, and Billy, his face red and his feet over-large, nearly knocked the box over as he got a paper out. "Tessie," Mr. Summers said. She hesitated for a minute, looking around defiantly, and then set her lips and went up to the box. She snatched a paper out and held it behind her.

"Bill," Mr. Summers said, and Bill Hutchinson reached into the box and felt around, bringing his hand out at last with the slip of paper in it.

The crowd was quiet. A girl whispered, "I hope it's not Nancy," and the sound of the whisper reached the edges of the crowd.

"It's not the way it used to be," Old Man Warner said clearly. "People ain't the way they used to be."

"All right," Mr. Summers said. "Open the papers. Harry, you open little Dave's."

Mr. Graves opened the slip of paper and there was a general sigh through the crowd as he held it up and everyone could see that it was blank. Nancy and Bill, Jr., opened theirs at the same time, and both beamed and laughed, turning around to the crowd and holding their slips of paper above their heads.

"Tessie," Mr. Summers said. There was a pause, and then Mr. Summers looked at Bill Hutchinson, and Bill unfolded his paper and showed it. It was blank.

"It's Tessie," Mr. Summers said, and his voice was hushed. "Show us her paper, Bill."

Bill Hutchinson went over to his wife and forced the slip of paper out of her hand. It had a black spot on it, the black spot Mr. Summers had made the night before with the heavy pencil in the coal-company office. Bill Hutchinson held it up, and there was a stir in the crowd.

"All right, folks," Mr. Summers said. "Let's finish quickly."

Although the villagers had forgotten the ritual and lost the original black box, they still remembered to use stones. The pile of stones the boys had made earlier was ready; there were stones on the ground with the blowing scraps of paper that had come out of the box. Mrs. Delacroix selected a stone so large she had to pick it up with both hands and turned to Mrs. Dunbar. "Come on," she said. "Hurry up."

Mrs. Dunbar had small stones in both hands, and she said, gasping for breath, "I can't run at all. You'll have to go ahead and I'll catch up with you."

The children had stones already, and someone gave little Davy Hutchinson a few pebbles.

Tessie Hutchinson was in the center of a cleared space by now, and she held her hands out desperately as the villagers moved in on her. "It isn't fair," she said. A stone hit her on the side of the head.

Old Man Warner was saying, "Come on, come on, everyone." Steve Adams was in the front of the crowd of villagers, with Mrs. Graves beside him.

"It isn't fair, it isn't right," Mrs. Hutchinson screamed, and then they were upon her.

FLORENCE ENGEL RANDALL

The Watchers

From the moment Althea awoke that morning, she knew their building had been chosen. She knew it even before she saw the excitement in her husband's eyes as he handed her the official notice that had been put under their door.

"Well," he said, smiling at her while she read it, "what do you think of that?"

"I had a feeling, George," she said, "even before I opened my eyes, I had a feeling that this would happen today."

"We were due to be next," George said. "The setup here is about perfect for it."

"Will you be home early?" She watched him while he sipped his coffee.

"It won't start until late," he said. "It won't start until it gets dark. You know how these things are."

"Just the same," she said, "I couldn't bear it just sitting around and waiting for you. We have so much to do. We have to have dinner first and then change our clothes and find seats. We want to have good seats," she reminded him. "They won't reserve any for us, you know."

"Don't worry about it." He touched her cheek lightly with the back of his hand. "I'll be home in plenty of time."

"Do you have everything? I was never so scared in my life yesterday when I found your gun on the top of the dresser. I just couldn't believe my eyes. I wanted to run after you but I didn't know which route you had taken."

"I always carry a spare," he said. "You know that. I always keep a spare in my coat pocket. Why don't you trust me?"

"I know I'm being foolish," Althea said, kissing him goodbye. "Just be careful, that's all. I don't want you to be so sure of yourself that you'll get careless."

"You be careful," he said. "Do you have to go out today?"

She frowned. "I have to go marketing, and then I thought I'd go downtown and buy a new dress for tonight. All the women will be dressed up and I don't want to go looking like a frump."

"Watch out for the department stores," he reminded her. "They can be dangerous. Don't take any crowded elevators and check the dressing room before you try anything on."

She locked and double-locked the door after him, then fastened the chain before she had her own breakfast. Standing at the window while she drank her coffee, she thought how ridiculous it was the way they went through the same routine each morning as if the very fact that they had to take precautions was making them nervous. When they were first married two years ago, it would never have occurred to either of them that there was any reason for worry.

It must be because we're so much in love, she told herself, stacking the dishes in the washer. Love breeds its own vulnerability, its own fear.

When the signal flashed on the wall, Althea had just finished dressing. She watched it for a moment. It was their code, all right. Three lights in a row, the flickering pause, and then the slow, deliberate hold. She pressed the button that buzzed downstairs.

"Who is it?" she said, her mouth against the intercom.

"It's all right," said a woman's voice, clear and high and a bit too shrill. "I've already shown my identification to your doorman. I'm Sally Milford — Cary Milford's wife. My husband works in your husband's office."

"What do you want?" said Althea cautiously. "I'm much too busy to see anyone this morning. Besides, I'm on my way out." She bit her lip. George would be right if he scolded her for being careless. Why had she told this woman she was going out?

"I'll only take a moment of your time. It's important."

"Can't you tell me what it is over the intercom?"

"If I wanted to talk this way, I could have called you on the phone. I must see you. Please."

"All right," said Althea reluctantly, knowing she was being foolish, "you can come up."

She checked her own gun even though she knew it was loaded and she palmed the small dagger — the one her mother had given her as a wedding present — the one with the jeweled handle.

"Things are so different now," her mother had said, sighing. She had lifted the dagger from the tissue paper and had studied it for a moment before she handed it to Althea. "In my day we could walk the streets without this sort of thing."

"That's not true," Althea reminded her. "You told me you used to wear stilt-like heels and you always carried a whistle in your purse."

"But that's not the same. It still wasn't like this," said her mother. "Did you know we weren't allowed to carry weapons?"

"You weren't?" said Althea, startled.

"That was before everyone realized that our laws were lagging behind our customs and public opinion. That was before the Citizen's Defense Act was passed."

"There is only one crime," Althea said firmly, "and that is to be a victim. Nothing makes sense otherwise."

"I suppose not." Her mother shook her head. "I guess I'm just being sentimental," she added wistfully. "Sometimes I miss the policemen we used to have. They would wear blue uniforms and they would drive around with sirens blaring and lights flashing. It seems a shame they became obsolete. Why I can even remember the time when we could take a walk in the park."

"In the park?" said Althea, incredulous. "You could actually do that?"

Now Althea bit her lip. There was no point in daydreaming. She stationed herself at the one-way peephole. The woman who now came within her range of vision was thin of face and well-dressed. She blinked her eyes nervously and hesitated before she knocked.

"Just a moment," said Althea. She unfastened the chain and the two locks, and then stepped back so that when the door opened she would be behind it. "Come in," she said.

"Where are you?"

"Right behind you," said Althea, her hand on her gun. "You're not very smart to walk right in like that, are you?"

"But I know who you are," said Sally Milford, her eyes wide with fright. "My husband and your husband are good friends."

"The first thing you have to learn," said Althea, "is not to trust anyone." She kicked the door shut. "Hold up your hands." She found a small acid gun in Sally's purse and a knife in the pocket of her jacket. "Just put them on the table," Althea directed, "and then sit down. Would you like some coffee?"

Sally shook her head, "Look," she said, her mouth trembling, "I wouldn't trouble you like this — I wouldn't have come at all if I didn't, in a way, know you. You see that, don't you?"

"No," said Althea firmly, "I don't see anything. Suppose you tell me what you want."

Sally clasped her hands on the edge of the table. "I have a brother-in-law who knows someone on the Board of Commissioners," she said, leaning forward in her eagerness, "and we heard that your apartment house has been chosen."

"These things are supposed to be a secret," Althea said sharply. "No one except the people involved is supposed to know. Don't you realize what can happen to you if they find out? And what can happen to me?"

"I'm sorry but I just couldn't help it. When I heard about it — all I could think was that I simply had to go. I have never been to a performance and, the way things look, I'll never have a chance."

"Where do you live?" Althea asked, putting the gun away.

"On the East Side. You know how safe it's getting to be over there. We haven't had an incident in months."

"That doesn't mean they won't choose your building eventually."

"Do you really think they will?"

"Why not?" said Althea.

"Then, in that case, why can't you make believe that we're visiting you or something? They do have special passes for visitors and then, when we're finally chosen, we could reciprocate. Cary and I could invite you and George. That way we could each see two performances."

"It wouldn't work," said Althea. "In the first place, we have the perfect setting for this sort of thing. That's why we picked this particular apartment building. We could have had a much better place to live but both George and I agreed that our best chance was being here. We had to wait two years for this day, and if they ever suspect that this was a put-up thing, you know what would happen to us."

"I suppose I was foolish to even hope." Sally stood up. "I thought it would work out."

"It won't," said Althea, feeling a sudden pity for her. "Believe me, Sally, it won't. I happen to know that Mrs. Tremont, who lives on the third floor, has her sister-in-law staying with her; that, of course, makes it possible for her sister-in-law to go tonight, but if she had just arrived today someone would be sure to report it and Mrs. Tremont would get into trouble."

"You said you were going out," said Sally. "Do you want a ride with me?"

"I'm going downtown," said Althea. "I thought I'd buy a new dress for tonight."

"I haven't been shopping in ages," said Sally. "Cary won't let me go without him and he's been much too busy on Saturdays. We could shop together and maybe have lunch."

"Just remember one thing," Althea warned as she reached for her coat and hat. "No matter what you say, I won't change my mind. You can spend the whole day with me if you like but I still won't change my mind."

"I know you're right," said Sally as they pressed the button for the elevator. "It's just that I'm glad to have some company on the subway."

"Are you still taking the subway?" Althea stared at her, amazed. "George insists that I take the bus. Not taxis — they're not too reliable anymore but a bus is still fine."

"It takes too long," said Sally. "The subway is much quicker. I have my own system. I never wait on a platform if I'm alone and I usually ride in the first car where the motorman is and, just in case anyone is following me, I change at every other stop."

"Now," said Althea, watching as the elevator stopped at their floor, "run!"

They pounded through the corridor and down one flight of steps. Then they rang for the elevator again. When it arrived, it was empty and they rode it the rest of the way down.

It turned out to be, Althea told George later, a rather pleasant day. With the two of them together, the shopping proved much easier. Sally stood watch while Althea tried on dresses and Althea stood guard while Sally shopped. When they finally parted, it was after four.

Althea took a bus uptown again and got off three blocks before her destination. She glanced behind to make sure she wasn't being followed; then she bought a steak at the meat market. Steak would be the quickest thing to cook for dinner and she didn't want to load her arms with too many packages. It was difficult enough carrying the dress, although she had insisted that the clerk put it in a shopping bag instead of a box. With a shopping bag she would feel less clumsy and have one hand free.

The doorman beamed at her when she entered the lobby.

"This is a great day for us," he said.

Althea nodded. "I bought a new dress," she told him happily, "a black sheath."

"I'll ride the elevator with you if you like," he offered generously. "Most of the tenants are home by now."

"You're not supposed to leave your post," Althea reminded him. "Anyone could come in while you were away. You know what happened to the last doorman we had?"

"You're right," he admitted. "For a moment I forgot."

"By the way," she whispered, "do you know who will be giving the performance?"

He shook his head. "No one knows," he said. "I've been asking but no one knows for sure. I think it's a young one. They usually are."

"You'd think those kids could learn," said Althea, ringing for the elevator. "My parents were pretty strict with me — I can tell you that."

"That's the best way," the doorman said. "You have to be firm with them. I always say that from the time they can walk, they can be taught. Now, you take that kid of Mrs. Hammond. You know the Hammonds on the fifth floor? He got his first slash today and was sent home from school in disgrace."

"Oh, no," said Althea, in horror. "He's only eleven. He's only allowed two more mistakes."

"The way Mrs. Hammond spanked him, he'll learn," the doorman said. "That'll never happen to him again, I can tell you that."

"Who was the other boy?"

"It was a girl," said the doorman. "A pretty little thing, I understand. Well, she'll get her first gold star for that."

"I got a gold star when I was twelve," said Althea, stepping into the elevator.

She rode it to the fourth floor and got out. She took the stairs the rest of the way, then stood before her own front door for a moment, listening. When she was positive it was safe, she inserted her key in the lock.

At precisely six o'clock George came home and, by seven thirty, they had finished dinner and were dressed.

"I'd like to go now," said Althea, impatiently.

"It won't get dark until eight," George said. "You know how it is this time of year. Even then, we'll have to wait a while."

"I can see the stands from here," said Althea, craning her neck as she peered out of the window. "People are beginning to arrive now. Please, darling, let's go."

"You're like a child," he said, hugging her. "Just an anxious little kid."

"I can't help it," she said. "I'm excited. Aren't you thrilled, George?"

"Come on," he said, indulgently. He looked at her, chic and lovely in her new black sheath. "No pockets," he said, shaking his head. "What made you buy a dress without any pockets? I didn't know they made them that way anymore."

"I'll only wear it when I'm with you," she said. "Besides, I have a knife in my purse."

"Just see that you keep it handy." He held the door for her. "I'm glad you used your head this morning."

"For a moment I was tempted," Althea confessed. "Sally seems like a sweet person and it might be fun if we could go there sometimes, but then I realized we'd be taking a chance."

"It doesn't pay to take chances," said George. "Otherwise you can end up giving the performance instead of watching it."

"The doorman told me it was a young one. Probably a girl."

"It usually is," said George.

"Do you know what she did?" Althea asked as they walked through the back of the lobby and out into the courtyard. "No one seems to know what she did."

"Probably something stupid," said George, looking around and waving to their neighbors. "You know, honey, you were right. The stands are filling up."

The stands had been placed next to their building. They were permanent, sturdily built of brick and stone, and erected when the building itself had been new. Optimistically every building had its stands ready for the day when it would be chosen, and Althea looked around proudly as she and George found seats in the second row.

Mr. and Mrs. Hammond were there and seated between them was their son, Timmy. Timmy's right arm was bandaged and he huddled close to his mother.

"I heard about it," said Althea, with sympathy. "I'm sure Timmy will never let it happen again."

"Because she was pretty. Because it was a girl," said Mrs. Hammond bitterly. "She called to him and he ran right over, leaving his knife in his pocket as if a knife ever did anybody any good in a pocket. Just because it was a little girl, he trusted her. But he's learned his lesson, haven't you, Timmy?" she said, slapping him across the face.

"No more," Timmy wept, putting his bandaged arm across his eyes. "Please, Mommy, don't hit me anymore."

He'll never amount to anything, Althea thought, staring at him in dismay. Only three chances and he's used up one already. He's too soft. When I have a child —

She thought about it for a moment, longing for a child but the apartment they were in was too small and they hadn't wanted to move until they had a chance at a performance. Maybe now — maybe now that they were finally spectators — perhaps now that the longed-for, dreamed-about moment had finally arrived, they could move to a larger place and she would have a child.

"You have to train them from the beginning," she whispered to George.

"Sure," he said, knowing what she meant. "It won't happen to us."

"It won't happen to us," she agreed, seeing the way George, even now, even at this moment of pleasure and relaxation, kept his hand in his pocket; George's hand curled over the bulge of his gun.

Althea leaned back. She had known, of course, what the stage setting would be but, just the same, sitting there, part of the expectant, eager audience, she had to admire its reality.

It represented a street scene. It could have been Althea's own street with its middle-class, red-brick buildings, the old-fashioned canopies extending from the wide entrances to the edge of the curb. Behind the lighted windows of the buildings, Althea could see the people, all the families together, having dinner, watching television, reading, talking, laughing — all the people of the city settling down for the night.

In the center of the stage was a street lamp, still unlit although it was twilight now; on the far right, there was a fire hydrant. The first floor of the center building was occupied by a shop. The sign said, "ANTIQUES," and Althea could see the lovely things in the window — the paintings in the carved, ornate frames, the delicate crystal goblets, a curved brass bowl. Suddenly the street light went on, dominating the center of the stage with its soft, gentle glow.

The curtain is rising, thought Althea, taking a deep breath. She always loved that moment in the theater, that magic moment when all the murmuring and the movement and the whispering stopped, the hush and wonder when the curtain rose and the stage lay there before them, the play ready to begin.

Someone somewhere in the back coughed and Althea drew a deep, sighing gasp of impatience.

The stage became alive. From the center building a man emerged, a nondescript man walking his dog at night. The dog tugged and the man whistled softly between his teeth as the two of them walked down the street. The stage became empty again and Althea clasped her hands in her lap, amazed to discover that they were shaking.

At the far right two shadows blurred, moved, took form. Now a girl and a boy strolled down the street. His arm was flung around her shoulders and, from the way she smiled at him, Althea knew they were in love. They moved slowly across the stage. They stopped before the antique shop and the girl pointed to the brass bowl and the boy nodded and gestured expansively, showing her there was nothing in the world he wouldn't get for her. They disappeared on the far left and the stage was empty again.

Althea unclasped her hands and, because her palms were wet, she rubbed them furtively together. Beside her she could hear the sound of George's breathing, slow, heavy, as if each breath were an effort.

Onstage, in the lighted backdrop, in the center building, some of the windows began to darken as if the occupants were retiring for the night.

It's getting late, thought Althea, watching. The lights are

dimming all over the city. People are yawning and stretching and getting into bed and even the sounds of the distant traffic seem muted as if someone had muffled all the rolling wheels.

A shadow, part of the shadow of the building, almost part of the square shape of the center building, took on form, and Althea saw that it was a man, a man who had been there all the time, hiding there without her being conscious of his presence.

From the far right she could hear the clicking of high heels on the pavement. Someone else, she thought, will walk down this street this night.

There was a rustle and a stir in the stands.

"Please, Mommy," Timmy whispered. "I don't want to stay here."

"Oh, you'll stay all right," said Mrs. Hammond grimly. "You just open your eyes wide. You watch everything, Timmy Hammond, if you know what's good for you."

"Be quiet down there," someone hissed. "Do you want to spoil everything?"

Althea gripped George's arm.

The footsteps grew louder and a girl came into view, entering downstage from the right. The shadow that was the man moved, and then became very still, waiting.

The girl moved across the stage. She paused under the street light. She touched the lamppost as if the feel of it under her fingers gave her some sort of reassurance. She hesitated, reluctant to leave the light.

Althea could see her clearly now. She was very young. She could be no more than nineteen — perhaps twenty. She wore a red suit and a little red beret with a feather stuck jauntily in it and her handbag was tucked under her arm. Her hair was blond and it tumbled loose over her shoulders.

Althea watched absorbed as the second figure moved again, the man crouching and then straightening as he ran toward the light, toward the girl in the red suit. At the clear view of his black-jacketed, black-clad figure, there was a sudden roar of applause. Althea clapped until her hands ached.

Out of the dark, into the light, he moved. The girl had her back toward him, not seeing him as the watchers saw him — sinuous, beautiful in his grace, tall, broad of shoulder, his hair allowed to grow long in back and his black cap set on the back of his head. The knife in his hand caught the light and sparkled.

He ran and then stopped. Deliberately, he stalked her. Professional that he was, he began to move slowly, coming down light on the balls of his feet.

The girl whirled around and, at the sight of him, she made a little whimpering sound in her throat. Her back now to the audience, she darted to the left and, as if they were part of a rigid dance pattern, the man stepped after her. She turned and ran to the right, her heels clicking frantically but he was there before her.

"Please," said the girl in the red suit. She darted back to the lamppost, back where the light was the brightest, where she could be seen most clearly. She turned and faced the backdrop, faced the buildings, the windows where the people were. Her right hand still clutched her purse, her left was now at her throat.

"Oh, please." Her voice rose to a keening wail of terror and anguish.

"Please," she screamed, her voice begging, her body begging. Then blindly she turned again and ran.

This cry in the night had awakened the sleepers. It had roused the dreamers. The darkened windows in the backdrop were illuminated again. Figures moved; there were silhouettes framed in the windows. The sleepers were awake. The dreamers had stopped dreaming and the city was alert and watching.

"Help me."

The city held its breath and listened.

"Please, help me."

But, Althea saw, she couldn't run far enough. She couldn't run fast enough. The man had her pinned against the wall now, pinned against the lighted, listening backdrop of the building and her handbag fell to the ground.

"I beg you." She was almost hidden by the man's bulk as he bent over her. "Won't somebody help me?"

The man in the black jacket raised his arm and the knife flashed. The girl screamed in agony, her cheek now as crimson as her suit. Dodging under his arms, she ran again, the slowing rhythm of her clicking heels the only sound to be heard.

The man watched her for a moment. The quiet, lighted windows watched and the filled stands watched. The man stood very still as if he were resting and then, gracefully, quickly, easily, he caught her again.

That does it, thought Althea, her heart pounding; that does it.

The knife gleamed and Althea held her breath. The arm lifted. The black-draped arm lifted and fell, lifted and fell. The red suit crumpled, falling as if it were empty, the red suit only a splotch now on the pavement. Then the man moved toward the hushed, absorbed watchers.

And there he stood, bowing and smiling, the knife dripping red at his side. Over and over again he took his bow while they all gave him the ultimate, the supreme tribute of their silence.

FLANNERY O'CONNOR

A Good Man Is Hard to Find

The grandmother didn't want to go to Florida. She wanted to visit some of her connections in east Tennessee and she was seizing at every chance to change Bailey's mind. Bailey was the son she lived with, her only boy. He was sitting on the edge of his chair at the table, bent over the orange sports section of the *Journal*. "Now look here, Bailey," she said, "see here, read this," and she stood with one hand on her thin hip and the other rattling the newspaper at his bald head. "Here this fellow that calls himself The Misfit is aloose from the Federal Pen and headed toward Florida and you read here what it says he did to these people. Just you read it. I wouldn't take my children in any direction with a criminal like that aloose in it. I couldn't answer to my conscience if I did."

Bailey didn't look up from his reading so she wheeled around then and faced the children's mother, a young woman in slacks, whose face was as broad and innocent as a cabbage and was tied around with a green head-kerchief that had two points on the top like a rabbit's ears. She was sitting on the sofa, feeding the baby his apricots out of a jar. "The children have been to Florida before," the old lady said. "You all ought to take them somewhere else for a change so they would see different parts of the world and be broad. They never have been to east Tennessee."

The children's mother didn't seem to hear her but the eight-year-old boy, John Wesley, a stocky child with glasses, said, "If you don't want to go to Florida, why dontcha stay at home?" He and the little girl, June Star, were reading the funny papers on the floor.

"She wouldn't stay at home to be queen for a day," June Star said without raising her yellow head.

"Yes and what would you do if this fellow, The Misfit, caught you?" the grandmother asked.

"I'd smack his face," John Wesley said.

"She wouldn't stay at home for a million bucks," June Star said. "Afraid she'd miss something. She has to go everywhere we go."

"All right, Miss," the grandmother said. "Just remember that the next time you want me to curl your hair."

June Star said her hair was naturally curly.

The next morning the grandmother was the first one in the car, ready to go. She had her big black valise that looked like the head of a hippopotamus in one corner, and underneath it she was hiding a basket with Pitty Sing, the cat, in it. She didn't intend for the cat to be left alone in the house for three days because he would miss her too much and she was afraid he might brush against one of the gas burners and accidentally asphyxiate himself. Her son, Bailey, didn't like to arrive at a motel with a cat.

She sat in the middle of the back seat with John Wesley and June Star on either side of her. Bailey and the children's mother and the baby sat in front and they left Atlanta at eight forty-five with the mileage on the car at 55890. The grandmother wrote this down because she thought it would be interesting to say how many miles they had been when they got back. It took them twenty minutes to reach the outskirts of the city.

The old lady settled herself comfortably, removing her white cotton gloves and putting them up with her purse on the shelf in front of the back window. The children's mother still had on slacks and still had her head tied up in a green kerchief, but the grandmother had on a navy blue straw sailor hat with a bunch of white violets on the brim and a navy blue dress with a small white dot in the print. Her collars and cuffs were white organdy trimmed with lace and at her neckline she had pinned a purple spray of cloth violets containing a sachet. In case of an accident, anyone seeing her dead on the highway would know at once that she was a lady.

She said she thought it was going to be a good day for driving, neither too hot nor too cold, and she cautioned Bailey that the speed limit was fifty-five miles an hour and that the patrolmen hid themselves behind billboards and small clumps of trees and sped out after you before you had a chance to slow down. She pointed out interesting details of the scenery: Stone Mountain; the blue granite that in some places came up to both sides of the highway; the brilliant red clay banks slightly streaked with purple; and the various crops that made rows of green lace-work on the ground. The trees were full of silver-white sunlight and the meanest of them sparkled. The children were reading comic magazines and their mother had gone back to sleep.

"Let's go through Georgia fast so we won't have to look at it much," John Wesley said.

"If I were a little boy," said the grandmother, "I wouldn't talk about my native state that way. Tennessee has the mountains and Georgia has the hills."

"Tennessee is just a hillbilly dumping ground," John Wesley said, "and Georgia is a lousy state too."

"You said it," June Star said.

"In my time," said the grandmother, folding her thin veined fingers, "children were more respectful of their native states and their parents and everything else. People did right then. Oh look at the cute little pickaninny!" she said and pointed to a Negro child standing in the door of a shack. "Wouldn't that make a picture, now?" she asked and they all turned and looked at the little Negro out of the back window. He waved.

"He didn't have any britches on," June Star said.

"He probably didn't have any," the grandmother explained. "Little niggers in the country don't have things like we do. If I could paint, I'd paint that picture," she said.

The children exchanged comic books.

The grandmother offered to hold the baby and the children's mother passed him over the front seat to her. She set him on her knee and bounced him and told him about the things they were passing. She rolled her eyes and screwed up her mouth and stuck her leathery thin face into his smooth bland one. Occasionally he gave her a faraway smile. They passed a large cotton field with five or six graves fenced in the middle of it, like a small island. "Look at the graveyard!" the grandmother said, pointing it out. "That was the old family burying ground. That belonged to the plantation."

"Where's the plantation?" John Wesley asked.

"Gone With the Wind," said the grandmother. "Ha. Ha."

When the children finished all the comic books they had brought, they opened the lunch and ate it. The grandmother ate a peanut butter sandwich and an olive and would not let the children throw the box and the paper napkins out the window. When there was nothing else to do they played a game by choosing a cloud and making the other two guess what shape it suggested. John Wesley took one the shape of a cow and June Star guessed a cow and John Wesley said, no, an automobile, and June Star said he didn't play fair, and they began to slap each other over the grandmother.

The grandmother said she would tell them a story if they would keep quiet. When she told a story, she rolled her eyes and waved her head and was very dramatic. She said once when she was a maiden lady she had been courted by a Mr. Edgar Atkins Teagarden from Jasper, Georgia. She said he was a very good-looking man and a gentleman and that he brought her a watermelon every Saturday with his initials cut in it, E. A. T. Well, one Saturday, she said, Mr. Teagarden brought the watermelon and there was nobody at home and he left it on the front porch and returned in his buggy to Jasper, but she never got the watermelon, she said, because a nigger boy ate it when he saw the initials, E. A. T.!

This story tickled John Wesley's funny bone and he giggled and giggled but June Star didn't think it was any good. She said she wouldn't marry a man that just brought her a watermelon on Saturday. The grandmother said she would have done well to marry Mr. Teagarden because he was a gentleman and had bought Coca-Cola stock when it first came out and that he had died only a few years ago, a very wealthy man.

They stopped at The Tower for barbecued sandwiches. The Tower was a part stucco and part wood filling station and dance hall set in a clearing outside of Timothy. A fat man named Red Sammy Butts ran it and there were signs stuck here and there on the building and for miles up and down the highway saying, TRY RED SAMMY'S FAMOUS BARBECUE. NONE LIKE FAMOUS RED SAMMY'S! RED SAM! THE FAT BOY WITH THE HAPPY LAUGH. A VETERAN! RED SAMMY'S YOUR MAN!

Red Sammy was lying on the bare ground outside The Tower with his head under a truck while a gray monkey about a foot high, chained to a small chinaberry tree, chattered nearby. The monkey sprang back into the tree and got on the highest limb as soon as he saw the children jump out of the car and run toward him.

Inside, The Tower was a long dark room with a counter at one end and tables at the other and dancing space in the middle. They all sat down at a board table next to the nickelodeon and Red Sam's wife, a tall burnt-brown woman with hair and eyes lighter than her skin, came and took their order. The children's mother put a dime in the machine and played "The Tennessee Waltz," and the grandmother said that tune always made her want to dance. She asked Bailey if he would like to dance but he only glared at her. He didn't have a naturally sunny disposition like she did and trips made him nervous. The grandmother's brown eyes were very bright. She swayed her head from side to side and pretended she was dancing in her chair. June Star said play something she could tap to so the children's mother put in another dime and played a fast number and June Star stepped out onto the dance floor and did her tap routine.

"Ain't she cute?" Red Sam's wife said, leaning over the counter. "Would you like to come be my little girl?"

"No I certainly wouldn't," June Star said. "I wouldn't live in a broken-down place like this for a million bucks!" and she ran back to the table.

"Ain't she cute?" the woman repeated, stretching her mouth politely.

"Aren't you ashamed?" hissed the grandmother.

Red Sam came in and told his wife to quit lounging on the counter and hurry up with these people's order. His khaki trousers reached just to his hip bones and his stomach hung over them like a sack of meal swaying under his shirt. He came over and sat down at a table nearby and let out a combination sigh and yodel. "You can't win," he said. "You can't win," and he wiped his sweating red face off with a gray handkerchief. "These days you don't know who to trust," he said. "Ain't that the truth?"

"People are certainly not nice like they used to be," said the grandmother.

"Two fellers come in here last week," Red Sammy said, "driving a Chrysler. It was a old beat-up car but it was a good one and these boys looked all right to me. Said they worked at the mill and you know I let them fellers charge the gas they bought? Now why did I do that?"

"Because you're a good man!" the grandmother said at once.

"Yes'm, I suppose so," Red Sam said as if he were struck with this answer.

His wife brought the orders, carrying the five plates all at once without a tray, two in each hand and one balanced on her arm. "It isn't a soul in this green world of God's that you can trust," she said. "And I don't count nobody out of that, not nobody," she repeated, looking at Red Sammy.

"Did you read about that criminal, The Misfit, that's escaped?" asked the grandmother.

"I wouldn't be a bit surprised if he didn't attact this place right here," said the woman. "If he hears about it being here, I wouldn't be none surprised to see him. If he hears it's two cent in the cash register, I wouldn't be a tall surprised if he . . ."

"That'll do," Red Sam said. "Go bring these people their Co'-Colas," and the woman went off to get the rest of the order.

"A good man is hard to find," Red Sammy said. "Everything is getting terrible. I remember the day you could go off and leave your screen door unlatched. Not no more."

He and the grandmother discussed better times. The old lady said that in her opinion Europe was entirely to blame for the way things were now. She said the way Europe acted you would think we were made of money and Red Sam said it was no use talking about it, she was exactly right. The children ran outside into the white sunlight and looked at the monkey in the lacy chinaberry tree. He was busy catching fleas on himself and biting each one carefully between his teeth as if it were a delicacy.

They drove off again into the hot afternoon. The grandmother took cat naps and woke up every few minutes with her own snoring. Outside of Toombsboro she woke up and recalled an old plantation that she had visited in this neighborhood once when she was a young lady. She said the house had six white columns across the front and that there was an avenue of oaks leading up to it and two little wooden trellis arbors on either side in front where you sat down with your suitor after a stroll in the garden. She recalled exactly which road to turn off to get to it. She knew that Bailey would not be willing to lose any time looking at an old house, but the more she talked about it, the more she wanted to see it once again and find out if the little twin arbors were still standing. "There was a secret panel in this house," she said craftily, not telling the truth but wishing that she were, "and the story went that all the family silver was hidden in it when Sherman came through but it was never found . . ."

"Hey!" John Wesley said. "Let's go see it! We'll find it! We'll poke all the woodwork and find it! Who lives there? Where do you turn off at? Hey Pop, can't we turn off there?"

"We never have seen a house with a secret panel!" June Star shrieked. "Let's go to the house with the secret panel! Hey Pop, can't we go see the house with the secret panel!"

"It's not far from here, I know," the grandmother said. "It wouldn't take over twenty minutes."

Bailey was looking straight ahead. His jaw was as rigid as a horseshoe. "No," he said.

The children began to yell and scream that they wanted to see the house with the secret panel. John Wesley kicked the back of the front seat and June Star hung over her mother's shoulder and whined desperately into her ear that they never had any fun even on their vacation, that they could never do what THEY wanted to do. The baby began to scream and John Wesley kicked the back of the seat so hard that his father could feel the blows in his kidney.

"All right!" he shouted and drew the car to a stop at the side of the road. "Will you all shut up? Will you all just shut up for one second? If you don't shut up, we won't go anywhere."

"It would be very educational for them," the grandmother murmured.

"All right," Bailey said, "but get this: this is the only time we're going to stop for anything like this. This is the one and only time."

"The dirt road that you have to turn down is about a mile back," the grandmother directed. "I marked it when we passed."

"A dirt road," Bailey groaned.

After they had turned around and were headed toward the dirt road, the grandmother recalled other points about the house, the beautiful glass over the front doorway and the candle-lamp in the hall. John Wesley said that the secret panel was probably in the fireplace.

"You can't go inside this house," Bailey said. "You don't know who lives there."

"While you all talk to the people in front, I'll run around behind and get in a window," John Wesley suggested.

"We'll all stay in the car," his mother said.

They turned onto the dirt road and the car raced roughly along in a swirl of pink dust. The grandmother recalled the times when there were no paved roads and thirty miles was a day's journey. The dirt road was hilly and there were sudden washes in it and sharp curves on dangerous embankments. All at once they would be on a hill, looking down over the blue tops of trees for miles around, then the next minute, they would be in a red depression with the dust-coated trees looking down on them.

"This place had better turn up in a minute," Bailey said, "or I'm going to turn around."

The road looked as if no one had traveled on it in months.

"It's not much farther," the grandmother said and just as she said it, a horrible thought came to her. The thought was so embarrassing that she turned red in the face and her eyes dilated and her feet jumped up, upsetting her valise in the corner. The instant the valise moved, the newspaper top she had over the basket under it rose with a snarl and Pitty Sing, the cat, sprang onto Bailey's shoulder.

The children were thrown to the floor and their mother, clutching the baby, was thrown out the door onto the ground; the old lady was thrown into the front seat. The car turned over once and landed right-side-up in a gulch off the side of the road. Bailey remained in the driver's seat with the cat — gray-striped with a broad white face and an orange nose — clinging to his neck like a caterpillar.

As soon as the children saw they could move their arms and legs, they scrambled out of the car, shouting, "We've had an ACCIDENT!" The grandmother was curled up under the dashboard, hoping she was injured so that Bailey's wrath would not come down on her all at once. The horrible thought she had had before the accident was that the house she had remembered so vividly was not in Georgia but in Tennessee.

Bailey removed the cat from his neck with both hands and flung it out the window against the side of a pine tree. Then he got out of the car and started looking for the children's mother. She was sitting against the side of the red gutted ditch, holding the screaming baby, but she only had a cut down her face and a broken shoulder. "We've had an ACCIDENT!" the children screamed in a frenzy of delight.

"But nobody's killed," June Star said with disappointment as the grandmother limped out of the car, her hat still pinned to her head but the broken front brim standing up at a jaunty angle and the violet spray hanging off the side. They all sat down in the ditch, except the children, to recover from the shock. They were all shaking.

"Maybe a car will come along," said the children's mother hoarsely.

"I believe I have injured an organ," said the grandmother, pressing her side, but no one answered her. Bailey's teeth were clattering. He had on a yellow sport shirt with bright blue parrots designed in it and his face was as yellow as the shirt. The grandmother decided that she would not mention that the house was in Tennessee.

The road was about ten feet above and they could see only the tops of the trees on the other side of it. Behind the ditch they were sitting in there were more woods, tall and dark and deep. In a few minutes they saw a car some distance away on top of a hill, coming slowly as if the occupants were watching them. The grandmother stood up and waved both arms dramatically to attract their attention. The car continued to come on slowly, disappeared around a bend and appeared again, moving even slower, on top of the hill they had gone over. It was a big black battered hearse-like automobile. There were three men in it.

It came to a stop just over them and for some minutes, the driver looked down with a steady expressionless gaze to where they were sitting, and didn't speak. Then he turned his head and muttered something to the other two and they got out. One was a fat boy in black trousers and a red sweat shirt with a silver stallion embossed on the front of it. He moved around on the right side of them and stood staring, his mouth partly open in a kind of loose grin. The other had on khaki pants and a blue striped coat and a gray hat pulled down very low, hiding most of his face. He came around slowly on the left side. Neither spoke.

The driver got out of the car and stood by the side of it, looking down at them. He was an older man than the other two. His hair was just beginning to gray and he wore silver-rimmed spectacles that gave him a scholarly look. He had a long creased face and didn't have on any shirt or undershirt. He had on blue jeans that were too tight for him and was holding a black hat and a gun. The two boys also had guns.

"We've had an ACCIDENT!" the children screamed.

The grandmother had the peculiar feeling that the bespectacled man was someone she knew. His face was as familiar to her as if she had known him all her life but she could not recall who he was. He moved away from the car and began to come down the embankment, placing his feet carefully so that he wouldn't slip. He had on tan and white shoes and no socks, and his ankles were red and thin. "Good afternoon," he said. "I see you all had you a little spill."

"We turned over twice!" said the grandmother.

"Oncet," he corrected. "We seen it happen. Try their car and see will it run, Hiram," he said quietly to the boy with the gray hat.

"What you got that gun for?" John Wesley asked. "Whatcha gonna do with that gun?"

"Lady," the man said to the children's mother, "would you mind calling them children to sit down by you? Children make me nervous. I want all you all to sit down right together there where you're at."

"What are you telling US what to do for?" June Star asked.

Behind them the line of woods gaped like a dark open mouth. "Come here," said their mother.

"Look here now," Bailey began suddenly, "we're in a predicament! We're in . . ."

The grandmother shrieked. She scrambled to her feet and stood staring. "You're The Misfit!" she said. "I recognized you at once!"

"Yes'm," the man said, smiling slightly as if he were pleased in spite of himself to be known, "but it would have been better for all of you, lady, if you hadn't of reckernized me."

Bailey turned his head sharply and said something to his mother that shocked even the children. The old lady began to cry and The Misfit reddened.

"Lady," he said, "don't you get upset. Sometimes a man says things he don't mean. I don't reckon he meant to talk to you thataway."

"You wouldn't shoot a lady, would you?" the grandmother said and removed a clean handkerchief from her cuff and began to slap her eyes with it.

The Misfit pointed the toe of his shoe into the ground and made a little hole and then covered it up again. "I would hate to have to," he said.

"Listen," the grandmother almost screamed, "I know you're a good man. You don't look a bit like you have common blood. I know you must come from nice people!"

"Yes mam," he said, "finest people in the world." When he smiled he showed a row of strong white teeth. "God never made a finer woman than my mother and my daddy's heart was pure gold," he said. The boy with the red sweat shirt had come around behind them and was standing with his gun at his hip. The Misfit squatted down on the ground. "Watch them children, Bobby Lee," he said. "You know they make me nervous." He looked at the six of them huddled together in front of him and he seemed to be embarrassed as if he couldn't think of anything to say. "Ain't a cloud in the sky," he remarked, looking up at it. "Don't see no sun but don't see no cloud neither."

"Yes, it's a beautiful day," said the grandmother. "Listen," she said, "you shouldn't call yourself The Misfit because I know you're a good man at heart. I can just look at you and tell."

"Hush!" Bailey yelled. "Hush! Everybody shut up and let me handle this!" He was squatting in the position of a runner about to sprint forward but he didn't move.

"I pre-chate that, lady," The Misfit said and drew a little circle in the ground with the butt of his gun.

"It'll take a half a hour to fix this here car," Hiram called, looking over the raised hood of it.

"Well, first you and Bobby Lee get him and that little boy to step over yonder with you," The Misfit said, pointing to Bailey and John Wesley. "The boys want to ast you something," he said to Bailey. "Would you mind stepping back in them woods there with them?"

"Listen," Bailey began, "we're in a terrible predicament! Nobody realizes what this is," and his voice cracked. His eyes were as blue and intense as the parrots in his shirt and he remained perfectly still.

The grandmother reached up to adjust her hat brim as if she were going to the woods with him but it came off in her hand. She stood staring at it and after a second she let it fall on the ground. Hiram pulled Bailey up by the arm as if he were assisting an old man. John Wesley caught hold of his father's hand and Bobby Lee followed. They went off toward the woods and just as they reached the dark edge, Bailey turned and supporting himself against a gray naked pine trunk, he shouted, "I'll be back in a minute, Mamma, wait on me!"

"Come back this instant!" his mother shrilled but they all disappeared into the woods.

"Bailey Boy!" the grandmother called in a tragic voice but she found she was looking at The Misfit squatting on the ground in front of her. "I just know you're a good man," she said desperately. "You're not a bit common!"

"Nome, I ain't a good man," The Misfit said after a second as if he had considered her statement carefully, "but I ain't the worst in the world neither. My daddy said I was a different breed of dog from my brothers and sisters. 'You know,' Daddy said, 'it's some that can live their whole life out without asking about it and it's others has to know why it is, and this boy is one of the latters. He's going to be into everything!' " He put on his black hat and looked up suddenly and then away deep into the woods as if he were embarrassed again. "I'm sorry I don't have on a shirt before you ladies," he said, hunching his shoulders slightly. "We buried our clothes that we had on when we escaped and we're just making do until we can get better. We borrowed these from some folks we met," he explained.

"That's perfectly all right," the grandmother said. "Maybe Bailey has an extra shirt in his suitcase."

"I'll look and see terrectly," The Misfit said.

"Where are they taking him?" the children's mother screamed.

"Daddy was a card himself," The Misfit said. "You couldn't put anything over on him. He never got in trouble with the Authorities though. Just had the knack of handling them."

"You could be honest too if you'd only try," said the grandmother. "Think how wonderful it would be to settle down and live a comfortable life and not have to think about somebody chasing you all the time."

The Misfit kept scratching in the ground with the butt of his gun as if he were thinking about it. "Yes'm, somebody is always after you," he murmured.

The grandmother noticed how thin his shoulder blades were just behind his hat because she was standing up looking down on him. "Do you ever pray?" she asked.

He shook his head. All she saw was the black hat wiggle between his shoulder blades. "Nome," he said.

There was a pistol shot from the woods, followed closely by another. Then silence. The old lady's head jerked around. She could hear the wind move through the tree tops like a long satisfied insuck of breath. "Bailey Boy!" she called.

"I was a gospel singer for a while," The Misfit said. "I been most everything. Been in the arm service, both land and sea, at home and abroad, been twict married, been an undertaker, been with the railroads, plowed Mother Earth, been in a tornado, seen a man burnt alive oncet," and he looked up at the children's mother and the little girl who were sitting close together, their faces white and their eyes glassy; "I even seen a woman flogged," he said.

"Pray, pray," the grandmother began, "pray, pray . . ."

"I never was a bad boy that I remember of," The Misfit said in an almost dreamy voice, "but somewheres along the line I done something wrong and got sent to the penitentiary. I was buried alive," and he looked up and held her attention to him by a steady stare.

"That's when you should have started to pray," she said. "What did you do to get sent to the penitentiary that first time?"

"Turn to the right, it was a wall," The Misfit said, looking up again at the cloudless sky. "Turn to the left, it was a wall. Look up it was a ceiling, look down it was a floor. I forget what I done, lady. I set there and set there, trying to remember what it was I done and I ain't recalled it to this day. Oncet in a while, I would think it was coming to me, but it never come."

"Maybe they put you in by mistake," the old lady said vaguely.

"Nome," he said. "It wasn't no mistake. They had the papers on me."

"You must have stolen something," she said.

The Misfit sneered slightly. "Nobody had nothing I wanted," he said. "It was a head-doctor at the penitentiary said what I had done was kill my daddy but I known that for a lie. My daddy died in nineteen ought nineteen of the epidemic flu and I never had a thing to do with it. He was buried in the Mount Hopewell Baptist churchyard and you can go there and see for yourself."

"If you would pray," the old lady said, "Jesus would help you."

"That's right," The Misfit said.

"Well then, why don't you pray?" she asked trembling with delight suddenly.

"I don't want no hep," he said. "I'm doing all right by myself."

Bobby Lee and Hiram came ambling back from the woods. Bobby Lee was dragging a yellow shirt with bright blue parrots in it.

"Throw me that shirt, Bobby Lee," The Misfit said. The shirt came flying at him and landed on his shoulder and he put it on. The grandmother couldn't name what the shirt reminded her of. "No, lady," The Misfit said while he was buttoning it up, "I found out the crime don't matter. You can do one thing or you can do another, kill a man or take a tire off his car, because sooner or later you're going to forget what it was you done and just be punished for it."

The children's mother had begun to make heaving noises as if she couldn't get her breath. "Lady," he asked, "would you and that little girl like to step off yonder with Bobby Lee and Hiram and join your husband?"

"Yes, thank you," the mother said faintly. Her left arm dangled helplessly and she was holding the baby, who had gone to sleep, in the other. "Hep that lady up, Hiram," The Misfit said as she struggled to climb out of the ditch, "and Bobby Lee, you hold onto that little girl's hand."

"I don't want to hold hands with him," June Star said. "He reminds me of a pig."

The fat boy blushed and laughed and caught her by the arm and pulled her off into the woods after Hiram and her mother.

Alone with The Misfit, the grandmother found that she had lost her voice. There was not a cloud in the sky nor any sun. There was nothing around her but woods. She wanted to tell him that he must pray. She opened and closed her mouth several times before anything came out. Finally she found herself saying, "Jesus, Jesus," meaning, Jesus will help you, but the way she was saying it, it sounded as if she might be cursing.

"Yes'm," The Misfit said as if he agreed. "Jesus thown everything off balance. It was the same case with Him as with me except He hadn't committed any crime and they could prove I had committed one because they had the papers on me. Of course," he said, "they never shown me my papers. That's why I sign myself now. I said long ago, you get you a signature and sign everything you do and keep a copy of it. Then you'll know what you done and you can hold up the crime to the punishment and see do they match and in the end you'll have something to prove you ain't been treated right. I call myself The Misfit," he said, "because I can't make what all I done wrong fit what all I gone through in punishment."

There was a piercing scream from the woods, followed closely by a pistol report. "Does it seem right to you lady, that one is punished a heap and another ain't punished at all?"

"Jesus!" the old lady cried. "You've got good blood! I know you wouldn't shoot a lady! I know you come from nice people!

Pray! Jesus, you ought not to shoot a lady. I'll give you all the money I've got!"

"Lady," The Misfit said, looking beyond her far into the woods, "there never was a body that give the undertaker a tip."

There were two more pistol reports and the grandmother raised her head like a parched old turkey hen crying for water and called, "Bailey Boy, Bailey Boy!" as if her heart would break.

"Jesus was the only One that ever raised the dead," The Misfit continued, "and He shouldn't have done it. He thrown everything off balance. If He did what He said, then it's nothing for you to do but thow away everything and follow Him, and if He didn't, then it's nothing for you to do but enjoy the few minutes you got left the best way you can — by killing somebody or burning down his house or doing some other meanness to him. No pleasure but meanness," he said and his voice had become almost a snarl.

"Maybe He didn't raise the dead," the old lady mumbled, not knowing what she was saying and feeling so dizzy that she sank down in the ditch with her legs twisted under her.

"I wasn't there so I can't say He didn't," The Misfit said. "I wisht I had of been there," he said, hitting the ground with his fist. "It ain't right I wasn't there because if I had of been there I would of known. Listen, lady," he said in a high voice, "if I had of been there I would of known and I wouldn't be like I am now." His voice seemed about to crack and the grandmother's head cleared for an instant. She saw the man's face twisted close to her own as if he were going to cry and she murmured, "Why you're one of my babies. You're one of my children!" She reached out and touched him on the shoulder. The Misfit sprang back as if a snake had bitten him and shot her three times through the chest. Then he put his gun down on the ground and took off his glasses and began to clean them.

Hiram and Bobby Lee returned from the woods and stood over the ditch, looking down at the grandmother who half sat and half lay in a puddle of blood with her legs crossed under her like a child's and her face smiling up at the cloudless sky.

Without his glasses, The Misfit's eyes were red-rimmed and

pale and defenseless-looking. "Take her off and thow her where you thown the others," he said, picking up the cat that was rubbing itself against his leg.

"She was a talker, wasn't she?" Bobby Lee said, sliding down the ditch with a yodel.

"She would of been a good woman," The Misfit said, "if it had been somebody there to shoot her every minute of her life."

"Some fun!" Bobby Lee said.

"Shut up, Bobby Lee," The Misfit said. "It's no real pleasure in life."

H. H. MARTIN and RAY DOWE, JR.

The Ordeal of Chaplain Kapaun

He wore the cross of the Corps of Chaplains instead of the crossed rifles of the infantry, but he was, I think, the best foot soldier I ever knew, and the bravest man, and the kindest. His name was Emil Joseph Kapaun, and he was a priest of the Roman Catholic Church. But the men he served in the prison camps of Korea didn't care whether he was Catholic or Baptist, Lutheran or Presbyterian. To all of them, Catholic, Protestant and Jew alike, and to men who professed no formal faith at all, he was simply "father," and each of them, when trouble came, drew courage and hope and strength from him.

He's dead now, murdered by the Red Chinese, and his body lies in an unmarked grave somewhere along the Yalu. But the hundreds of men who knew and loved him have not forgotten him. And I write this so that the folks at home can know what kind of man he was, and what he did for us, and how he died.

The first thing I want to make clear is this: He was a priest of the Church, and a man of great piety, but there was nothing ethereal about him, nothing soft or unctuous or holier-than-thou. He wore his piety in his heart. Outwardly he was all GI, tough of body, rough of speech sometimes, full of the wry humor of the combat soldier. In a camp where men had to steal or starve, he was the most accomplished food thief of them all. In a prison whose inmates hated their communist captors with a bone-deep hate, he was the most unbending enemy of Communism, and when they tried to brain-wash him, he had the guts to tell them to their faces that they lied. He pitied the Reds for their delusions, but he preached no doctrine of turn-the-other-cheek. I came upon him once sitting in the sunshine by the road. There was a smile on his face and a look of happiness in his eyes.

I hated to break in on his meditations, but I needed cheering, so I asked him, "What are you thinking of, father?"

"Of that happy day," he said, "when the first American tank rolls down that road. Then I'm going to catch that little so-and-so, Comrade Sun, and kick him right over the compound fence."

Such plain, blunt speech was typical of him. He always spoke in phrases that the most unlettered soldier could understand, for he was the son of a Kansas farmer, and he had a farmer's flair for down-to-earth, homely talk. In his religious services, which he doggedly held even though the Chinese threatened him, his brief sermons were deep, but every point he made struck home. Even the great mysteries of the Christian faith, which no man can fully comprehend, became clearer to us as he talked of them. He always spoke in parallels, relating the suffering that Christ endured to those that we were forced to bear. As he spoke, the agony in the garden, the road to Calvary, the Crucifixion, became very real to us, who ourselves lived daily under the threat of death, and who bore our own crosses of blows, and cold, and illness, and starvation. But Christ endured, he told us, and we, too, must endure, for the day of our resurrection from the tomb of the prison camp would surely come, as surely as the stone was rolled away from the sepulchre. And because of these sermons, which gave us hope and courage, and the food he stole for us, and the care he gave us when we were sick, many of us came back who never would have survived our long ordeal without him.

He had become a legend among the troops long before the

Chinese captured him. When his outfit, the 8th Cavalry Regiment of the 1st Cavalry Division, was fighting along the Naktong, his jeep was blown up by enemy fire and his driver was wounded. So he commandeered a ramshackle bicycle. Helmet jammed down over his ears, pockets stuffed with apples and peaches he had scrounged from Korean orchards, he'd ride this bone-shaker over the rocky roads and the paths through the paddy fields until he came to the forward outposts. There he'd drop in a shallow hole beside a nervous rifleman, crack a joke or two, hand him a peach, say a little prayer with him and move on to the next hole. He always stayed close to the fighting. Even before the blood had dried on the dusty slopes after the Cav had taken a hill, he's set up his altar on a litter stretched across two ammunition boxes. There on the battlefield, with mortar fire coming in and the enemy massing for a counter-attack, he'd hear Confessions, and celebrate the Mass, and administer Holy Communion to men who in another hour would be in battle again. His parish was the front and the battalion aid station close behind the lines. There he'd cheer and comfort the wounded all he could. He'd joke and kid with the lightly wounded, and over the dying men, whatever their faith, he'd say the last prayers of the Church. He seemed to have no fear that he himself might be killed. At Kumchon early in the war, when word came back that there was a wounded man on the left flank of the first battalion, in a position so exposed that the litter men could not reach him, father and another officer went after him and brought him back, crawling and ducking from rock to rock through fire so thick his pipe was shot out of his mouth.

It was his devotion to the wounded which finally cost him his freedom, and his life. It was at Unsan, on the second of November in 1950. For thirty-six hours the 8th Cavalry, fighting a perimeter defense, beat off a fanatical attack. Early in the morning the breakthrough came, and all day hand-to-hand fighting swirled around the command post and the aid station where the wounded lay. Finally, at dusk, the order came for every man who could still walk to try a breakout through the surrounding enemy. Father, who was unwounded, might have escaped with them. He refused to go. Of his own free will he stayed on, helping Captain Clarence L. Anderson, the regimental surgeon, take care of the wounded. And there, just at dark, the Chinese took him as he said the last prayers over a dying man.

I'll never forget the night I finally met him. It was at Pyoktong, on a backwater of the Yalu, a village where prisoners from many American units were being assembled. With the survivors of my outfit, C Company of the 19th Infantry of the 24th Division, I had been brought there from near Anju, where we had been overrun. The men of the 8th Cavalry who had broken out of the perimeter and had later been captured by twos and threes as they scattered to the south, were already there. As we came in, they crowded around us, asking for word of Father Kapaun. We had none.

That afternoon, Pyoktong was bombed. A B-26 swept over, dropping fire bombs, and more than half the city went up in flames. The Chinese panicked. They broke all the prisoners out of their houses and, shooting at the feet of the walking wounded to hurry them along, they herded us up onto a hill above the town. All that afternoon and into the night we sat there on the icy slope, cold and miserable, smoking cigarettes made of dried oak leaves and watching the burning town. That night they brought us down to where the wounded from another group lay along a road on litters made out of straw sacks stretched on rough pine poles. We shouldered their stretchers and set off over a frozen road to the southwest.

I was on the right-hand pole, at the front. We carried them on our shoulders, and as the shoulder began to ache with the pressure of the pole against the muscle, we'd stop and change round. It was during one of these breaks that I noticed the man who was carrying behind me. He was a short man, thick-shouldered, with wide-set gray eyes and a strong jaw with a deep cleft in it. He wore a thin, red-brown beard, with a little tuft of goat whiskers at the chin.

"I'm Mike Dowe," I said.

"Kapaun," he said, and put out his hand.

"Father!" I said, feeling as if I'd met an old friend. "I've heard about you."

He smiled. "Don't pass it along," he said. "It might get back to the Chief of Chaplains."

It was a feeble joke, but it cheered us all.

Hour after hour we stumbled on. It was hard enough to walk by yourself in the dark, on that slippery footing, but carrying a litter was agony. Father never ordered a man to carry. After a rest he'd just call, "Let's pick 'em up," and all down the line the guys would bend and lift, and follow him. Far in the night we came to a village of huts scattered along a narrow valley. The Chinese went ahead of us, driving the people out of the houses. We dropped all the wounded off at one house, and the rest of us were moved on to other houses farther up the valley. Father and Doctor Anderson refused to leave the wounded, but the Chinese threatened them and made them move on with the rest of us. The next morning they came around and pulled all the officers out and put us together in a compound at the north end of the valley. Father squawked about being separated from the enlisted men. But the Chinese poked him with gun butts and made him move along.

In the first week of our stay in the valley the Chinese allowed us a food ration of 500 grams of millet or cracked corn per man per day. It was a starvation ration to begin with, and then they cut it down to 450 grams. It was obvious, father said, that we must either steal food or slowly starve. And in that dangerous enterprise we must have the help of some power beyond ourselves. So, standing before us all, he said a prayer to St. Dismas, the Good Thief, who was crucified at the right hand of Jesus, asking for his aid.

I'll never doubt the power of prayer again. Father, it seemed, could not fail. At the risk of being shot by the guards he'd sneak at night into the little fields around the compound and prowl through the shocked corn, and find where the Koreans had hidden potatoes and grain beneath the corn shocks. He moved out of the crowded room where nineteen of us slept spoon-fashion on the dirt floor, to sleep in an open shed in the compound — and found that the shed backed up to a crib full of Korean corn, which he stole, surreptitiously, ear by ear.

His riskiest thefts were carried out by daylight under the noses of the Chinese. The POW's cooked their own food, which was drawn from an open supply shed some two miles down the valley. When men were called out to make the ration run, father would slip in at the end of the line. Before the ration detail reached the supply shed, he'd slide off into the bushes. Creeping and crawling, he'd come up behind the shed, and while the rest of us started a row with the guards and the Chinese doling out the rations, he'd sneak in, snatch up a sack of cracked corn and scurry off into the bushes with it. There were other men stealing, too, and some of them squirreled their stolen food away to eat themselves. Father tossed his into the common pot. He never said a word to the men who hid and hoarded food. But at night, after a successful foray, he'd say a prayer of thanks to God for providing food "which all can equally share." That seemed to shame them, and soon the private hoarding stopped.

His one great failure had overtones of humor which served to relieve what at the moment was black tragedy. Once, after we'd been moved back to Pyoktong, a little black pig wandered into the compound. Men who had tasted no meat in months felt themselves drooling as father, a big rock in his hand, cautiously stalked the pig. While a dozen silent prayers went up, he raised the stone high and brought it down. It struck the pig, but only a glancing blow. The pig set up a horrible squealing, the Chinese guard came running, slamming a cartridge into his rifle and shouting, "Huh?" "Huh?" "Huh?" Father fled for the latrine, and the guard, confused, ran down the road in hot pursuit of the pig.

Soon after we reached the valley, the wounded in the sick house — only the Chinese called it the hospital — began to die by dozens, poisoned by their untended wounds. Finally the Chinese allowed Doctor Anderson to go to their aid, though he had nothing but the skill of his hands to help them. Encouraged by this concession, father asked permission to go with the doctor. It was refused.

"What these men need is medicine, not prayer," the Chinese told him.

"Since they aren't getting any medicine," father answered, "a little prayer won't hurt."

"No," the Chinese said, "you will not be permitted to spread your poisonous Christian propaganda here."

Then began father's most hazardous exploits. On days when there was a ration run, he'd stop and steal food at the warehouse. Then, with his pockets full of cracked corn, or millet, dodging the Chinese roving patrols that watched the trail, he'd move on to the house where the wounded were. On days when there was no ration run or wood-carrying detail, he'd sneak there down the creek that ran through the valley, ducking under the bushes to keep out of sight of the guards along the road. He scrounged cotton undershirts to make bandages. He took their old bandages, foul with corruption, and sneaked them out and washed them and sneaked them back again. He picked the lice from their bodies, an inestimable service, for a man so weak he cannot pick his own lice soon will die. He let them smoke his pipe, loaded with dry cotton leaves, and he joked with them, and said prayers for them, and held them in his arms like children as delirium came upon them. But the main thing he did for them was to put into their hearts the will to live. For when you are wounded and sick and starving, it's easy to give up and quietly die.

Somehow, as it says in the Testament, "Power went forth from him and healed them." In Father Kapaun's valley the conditions were the same as in the camp known as Death Valley. But in Death Valley the death rate was ten times higher. Even when they died, he did not abandon them. The POW's buried their own dead, carrying the bodies up the adjacent mountainsides and later, in Pyoktong, across the frozen Yalu backwater to a little island where they dug the graves in the stony frozen ground. Men dodged this detail whenever they could. But father always volunteered. And at the grave as the earth covered the naked body — for the clothing of the dead was saved to warm the living — he would utter for them the last great plea: "Eternal rest grant unto him, O Lord, and let perpetual light shine upon him."

When he had done all he could at the house of the wounded he would slip out to the houses where the enlisted men were kept. He would step in quickly and quietly, saying, "The Lord be with you," and the starving, torpid men lying on the straw mats would sit up and respond, as he had taught them, "And with Thy Spirit." Then he would say a quick general service, beginning with a prayer for the men who had died in Korea, both in battle and in prison, and for the sick and wounded, and for the folks back home. Then he would say a prayer of thanks to God for the favors He had granted us, whether we know about them or not, "for the food and wood and water we have received at the hands of our enemies." Then he'd speak, very briefly, a short, simple sermon, urging them to hold on and not lose hope of freedom. And above all, he urged them not to fall for the lying doctrines the Reds were trying to pound into our heads. "Be not afraid of them who kill the body," he'd say, quoting from the Scriptures. "Fear ye him, who after he hath killed, hath power to cast into hell." To father's stubborn faith, the man who bought the communist teachings — and a very small group did out of ignorance or opportunism — was selling his immortal soul.

In his soiled and ragged fatigues, with his scraggly beard and his queer woolen cap, made of the sleeve of an old GI sweater, pulled down over his ears, he looked like any other half-starved prisoner. But there was something in his voice and bearing that was different — a dignity, a composure, a serenity that radiated from him like a light. Wherever he stood was holy ground, and the spirit within him — a spirit of reverence and abiding faith — went out to the silent, listening men and gave them hope and courage and a sense of peace. By his very presence, somehow, he could turn a stinking, louse-ridden mud hut, for a little while, into a cathedral.

He did a thousand little things to keep us going. He gathered and washed the foul undergarments of the dead and distributed them to men so weak from dysentery they could not move, and he washed and tended these men as if they were little babies. He traded his watch for a blanket, and cut it up to make warm socks for helpless men whose feet were freezing. All one day, in a freezing wind, with a sharp stick and his bare hands, he cut steps in the steep, ice-covered path that led down to the stream, so that the men carrying water would not fall. The most dreaded housekeeping chore of all was cleaning the latrines, and men argued bitterly over whose time it was to carry out this loathsome task. And while they argued, he'd slip out quietly and do the job.

In mid-January, in subzero cold, they marched us eight miles back to Pyoktong, into houses still shattered by the bombing and the fire. Nine of the sick and wounded died that day, and many of the rest of us, sick, half-starved and despairing, were on the point of giving up. But father led scrounging parties out, to prowl through the ruins to find nails and tin and broken boards to patch the houses and make them livable. In the yard of the officers' compound he built a little fireplace with bricks he had stolen. On it, with wood he had stolen — once they caught him stealing pickets from a fence and made him stand for hours, stripped of his outergarments, in the bitter cold — he would heat water in pans made from tin he had stolen and pounded into shape with a rock. Every morning he'd bring in this pan full of hot water, calling cheerfully, "Coffee, everybody," and pour a little into every man's bowl. And though there was no coffee in it, somehow this sip of hot water in the morning gave each man heart to rise and pick off his lice and choke down his bowl of soupy millet, and face, if not with cheerfulness, at least without despair, another day of captivity and abuse.

He was always telling us we'd soon be free, and he was always dreaming up fancy menus — ten-course meals we'd eat when we got home. At night we'd hear the roar and see the flash of great explosions to the south. It was our bombers, working over the roads and bridges on the Reds' supply routes to the front. But we thought it was our artillery. "The guns sound closer tonight," father would say. "They're coming. They'll be here soon. The moon is full tonight. By the time it's full again, we'll be free."

As weeks and months passed, robbed of all strength by pellagra and beriberi, men grew weaker. The unbroken diet of millet and corn became nauseating. We could hardly choke it down. By mid-March we were in desperate condition, boiling green weeds in our hunt for vitamins. The hideous swelling of the body that is the first mark of approaching death by starvation was showing up on more and more of us. The night before Saint Patrick's Day, father called us together and prayed to Saint Patrick, asking him to help us in our misery. The next day, the Chinese brought us a case of liver — the first meat we had had — and issued us *golian* instead of millet. The liver was spoiled and *golian* is sorghum seed, used as cattle feed in the States, but to us they were like manna. Later he prayed for tobacco, and that night a guard walked by and tossed a little bag of dry, straw-like Korean tobacco into our room.

As our bodies weakened, the Reds stepped up the pace of their propaganda assault upon our minds. Hour after hour we sat in lectures while Comrade Sun, a fanatic little Chinese who hated Americans with an insane hatred, assailed our rotten, capitalistic Wall Street civilization. Then we'd have to comment upon the great truths revealed by Comrade Sun. A few bold men, in reckless despair, commented in unprintable words of contempt and were thrown into a freezing hole or subjected to other severe tortures sometimes resulting in death. Some veiled their ridicule. "According to the great doctrines taught us by the noble Stalin, Lenin, Marx, Engels, Amos and Andy — " they would read aloud in the "classes."

Father was not openly arrogant, nor did he use subterfuge. Without losing his temper or raising his voice, he'd answer the lecturer point by point, with a calm logic that set Comrade Sun screaming and leaping on the platform like an angry ape.

Strangely, they never punished him, except by threats and ominous warnings. Two officers who knew him well were taken away and tortured. With their hands tied behind them, they were lifted by ropes until their wrist joints pulled apart. They then were brought back to accuse him publicly. They charged him with slandering the Chinese, which was true — if you call the real truth slander, as they did. They said he advocated resistance to the Reds' study program, and that he displayed a hostile attitude toward his captors, all of which was also true. They said he threatened men with courts-martial on their return if they went along with the Chinese, which was not true. Father never threatened anybody. When the two men came back after their ordeal, unsure of their welcome, father was the first to greet them. Looking at their twisted hands, he told them, "You never should have suffered a moment, trying to protect me."

We expected that the public accusation would bring on a farcical trial in which father would be convicted and taken out and never returned. Instead, they merely called him in and bullied him and threatened him. We realized then what we had half known all along. They were afraid of him. They recognized in him a strength they could not break, a spirit they could not quell. Above all things, they feared a mass rebellion, and they knew that if father was maltreated, the whole camp of 4,000 men would mutiny.

On Easter Sunday, 1951, he hurled at them his boldest challenge, openly flouting their law against religious services. In the yard of a burned-out church in the officers' compound, just at sunrise, he read the Easter service. He could not celebrate the Easter Mass, for all his Mass equipment had been lost at the time of his capture. All he had was the things he used when administering the last rites to the dying — the purple ribbon, called a stole, which he wore round his neck as a badge of his priesthood, the gold ciborium, now empty, in which the Host had been carried when he had administered Holy Communion, and the little bottles of holy oil used to administer the last sacraments. But he fashioned a cross out of two rough pieces of wood, and from a borrowed missal he read the stations of the Cross to the scarecrow men, sitting on the rubbled steps of the burned church. He told the story of Christ's suffering and death, and then, holding in his hands a Rosary made of bent barbed wire cut from the prison fence, he recited the glorious mysteries of Christ risen from the tomb and ascended into heaven.

As we watched him it was clear to us that father himself at last had begun to fail in strength. On the starvation diet we were allowed, a man could not miss a single day's meals without growing too weak to walk, and for months father had been sharing his meager rations with sick and dying men. The week after Easter he began to limp, hobbling along on a crooked stick. The next Sunday, as he read the service for the first Sunday after Easter, as he reached the line in the Epistle: "And this is the victory that overcomes the world, our Faith," his voice faltered, and we caught him as he fell.

Beneath his tattered uniform his right leg was dreadfully swollen and discolored. For weeks, we knew, he had been suffering terrible bone aches, a by-product of hunger, that came upon men at night with such fearful pain that they would scream and beat the ground in agony. Father, when awake, had never whimpered, though tears of pain filled his eyes. When he slept, though, his iron will broke, and he would moan pitifully. Finally, the bad pain went away, but the leg continued to swell until it was one great mass of purple, blue and yellow flesh. The communist "doctor," a brainwasher posing as a medical man, pronounced the usual diagnosis by which they sought to convince us — or themselves — that we were an evil, immoral and decaying race. Doctor Anderson and his medical companion, Captain Sidney Esensten, knew it for what it was — a blood clot blocking circulation to the leg.

They applied hot packs, and slowly the swelling began to subside. Soon father could walk again, though he was so weak and shaky he would often fall. Then a fearful dysentery seized him, and as he so often had done for us, we cared for him as best we could. And he beat that, and got on his feet again. Then, one raw, cold day he arose, a walking ghost, to give the last sacrament to a dying man. The next day his eyes were bright with fever and his breath came in a hoarse rattle. He had taken pneumonia, and soon was in delirium. Thinking back upon it, I believe that period of semi-consciousness was the only happy time he knew during his captivity. Around him there seemed to gather all the people he had known in his boyhood on the farm in Kansas and in his school days. Babbling happily, sometimes laughing, he spoke to his mother and his father, and to the priests he'd known in seminary. Even in his delirium, his unbreakable spirit manifested itself in sallies of humor. Finally, he sank into a deep and quiet sleep, and when he awoke, he was completely rational. The crisis had passed. He was getting well.

But the Chinese did not intend that he should live. He was sitting up, eating and cracking jokes, when the guards came with a litter to take him to the hospital. We knew then that he was doomed, for the hospital was no hospital at all, but a death house so dreadful that I will make no attempt to describe it here. In the room in which he was placed, men *in extremis* were left to lie untended in filth and freezing cold, until merciful death took them. The doctors protested violently against his being taken there, but the Chinese cursed them and forbade them to go along and care for him. The rest of us protested. All they answered was "He goes! He goes!"

Father himself made no protest. He looked around the room at all of us standing there, and smiled. He held in his hands the ciborium, the little covered cup in which, long ago, he had carried the blessed bread.

"Tell them back home that I died a happy death," he said, and smiled again.

As they loaded him on the litter he turned to Lieutenant Nardella, from whose missal he had read the services. He put the little book in Nardella's hand.

"You know the prayers, Ralph," he said. "Keep holding the services. Don't let them make you stop."

He turned to another officer, who, before his capture, had been having trouble at home.

"When you get back to Jersey, you get that marriage straightened out," he told him, "or I'll come down from heaven and kick you in the tail."

Then he turned to me.

"Don't take it hard, Mike," he said. "I'm going where I've always wanted to go. And when I get up there, I'll say a prayer for all of you."

I stood there, crying unashamed, as they took him down the road, the little gold cup still shining in his hand. Beside me stood Fezi Gurgin, a Turkish lieutenant, a Mohammedan.

"To Allah who is my God," said Fezi Bey, "I will say a prayer for him.

A few days later he was dead. Not long afterward, the little daughter of the Chinese camp commander walked past the compound gate. She was tossing up and catching something that glittered in the sun. It was father's little gold cup. On the demands of the POW's, it was returned at Big Switch. We brought it back to commemorate his deeds and the deeds of all who died at the hands of the communists. It is to be placed on a memorial in his home town.

A year later, on the anniversary of his death, Ralph Nardella asked the communists for permission to hold a service in his memory. They refused. I was glad they did. For it told me that even though he was dead, his body lost forever in a mass grave, they still were afraid of him. They feared him because he was the symbol of something they knew they could not kill — the unconquerable spirit of a free man, owing final allegiance only to his God. And in that sense, I know, he and the things he believed in can never die.

IRWIN SHAW

God on Friday Night

Sol let himself quietly into the house and walked softly down the long hall toward the kitchen, the only sound the fashionable creaking of his pale tan shoes. He saw his mother bending over the stove, red-faced, peering into the roaster, basting a chicken.

"Ma," he said softly.

Ma grunted, busily pushing the potatoes.

"It's me, Ma. It's Sol."

Ma closed the oven and stood up wearily, her hand pushing helpfully at the hip.

"Kiss Mama," she said.

Sol kissed her and she sat down and looked at him. "You don't look so good, Sol. You don't look the way you looked when you were a young boy."

Every time she saw him she told him the same thing.

"What do you want, Ma?" Sol sighed, voicing the hopeless argument. "I'm not a young boy any more. I'm a man thirty-three years old."

"Even so." Ma wiped her forehead and looked anxiously at him. "The life you lead."

"A man who makes his living entertaining in night clubs can't

---

live like a prize horse," Sol said. He sat down across the table and stretched his hand out tenderly to cover hers. "How're yuh, Ma?"

Ma sighed. "What do you expect? My kidneys. Always my kidneys. A woman with a family gets old like an express train." She looked closely at her son. "Sol, darling," she said, "you wear the worst clothes I've ever seen on a man's back. You belong on a merry-go-round."

"In my profession," Sol said with sober pride, "this is the way they dress."

"They should not be allowed out in the daytime." She shook her head. "That tie. That material would be good to line closets with."

"Violet picked out this tie."

"How is Violet? Why can't she come visit her mother-in-law once in a while? Is the Bronx another world?"

"Violet's all right," Sol said flatly, looking at the glitter on his shoe tips. "Only. . . ."

Ma sighed, her large, fashionably supported bosom heaving under the black net. "OK, Baby, tell Mama."

Sol leaned over anxiously. "I must talk to you private."

Ma looked around the kitchen. "Are we in Grand Central Station?"

"Real private, Ma. I don't want *nobody* to hear this. *Nobody.* Not even Pop."

"What've you done, Sol?" There was a note of stern alarm in Ma's voice, and she grabbed Sol's arm tightly. "Tell Mama the truth."

"I ain't done nothing. Honest. At least nothing bad. Don't worry, Ma."

"Nobody's sick?"

"Nobody's sick."

"All right." Ma sat back in her chair, holding her feet off the floor to take the weight off them. "Do you want to stay to dinner? You can always cut an extra portion out of a chicken."

"Lissen, Ma," Sol said intensely, "you got to lissen to me and you got to promise you won't tell nobody."

"I promise. All right, I promise. Will you stay to dinner?"

"Yeah," Sol said. "Well . . ." he hesitated, "this is complicated."

Lawrence came into the kitchen, throwing his books on the floor. "Hiya, Sol. Hello, Mom. Am I hungry, or, Momma, am I hungry. . . . Mom, whatta ye got to eat, or am I hungry!"

"I'm talkin' to Ma, private," Sol said.

"I'm hungry," Lawrence said, looking in the icebox. "Go ahead and talk. I'll forget it anyway."

"I want to talk to Ma private," Sol said in measured tones.

"What the hell's so private?" Lawrence asked, gesturing with a bottle of milk. "What're you, a German spy? Boy, am I hungry!"

"Don't say 'hell,' Larry," Ma said, "And get out of here."

"I'm taking the bottle with me," Lawrence announced, marching toward the door. He patted his mother on the head. "Mata Hari." He went out.

"A brilliant boy," Ma said. "He leads his class."

Sol cleared his throat.

"Yes, Sol," Ma said, "I'm listening."

"I been thinking, Ma," he began in a low thoughtful voice, twisting his heavy gold ring slowly around on his finger. "I ain't a good boy."

"That's not such private news." Ma laughed at the expression on Sol's face. She pinched his arm. "You got a good heart, Sol," she said. "My baby Sol, with a heart like a house."

"I have done things, Ma," Sol said slowly, choosing his words with great care, "that were not so good."

"If we were all angels, we wouldn't need airplanes," Ma said with finality. "Let me look at the chicken."

She went over and looked at the chicken. "That butcher!" she said. "He is selling me eagles." She closed the oven door and sat down again.

"I have done things," Sol said quietly, "that God wouldn't like."

"I think God has other things on His mind these days, Sol."

"Ma," Sol said, not looking at his mother, "Ma, would you light candles on Friday night and make the prayer?"

There was silence in the kitchen, broken only by the small crackle from the oven, where the chicken was browning.

"I haven't lighted candles for a long time, Sol," Ma said gently.

"Ever since the day I married your father. He was a Socialist, your father."

"Would yuh light 'em now, Ma?" Sol pleaded. "Every Friday night?"

"What is it, Sol? Why should I light candles?"

Sol took a deep breath and stood up and walked back and forth in the kitchen. "Violet," he said, "Violet's goin' to have a baby."

"Oh!" Ma gasped, fanning herself. "Oh! Well! That blonde girl! Oh! A grandchild! Oh! Sol, Baby!" She grabbed Sol and kissed him. "My Sol!"

"Don't cry, Ma. Ma, please. . . ." Sol patted her solid wide back. "It's all right."

"It's about time, Sol. I thought you'd never . . ." She kissed him on the forehead and smiled widely. "I thought Violet was beginning to look very good in the breasts. Congratulations from the bottom of my heart. We'll name him after my father."

"Yeah," Sol said. "Thanks. How about the candles now, Ma?"

"What do you need candles for? I had five children without burning a single candle."

"Violet's different," Sol said uneasily. "She's not like you."

"She is just built for children," Ma declared. "She is built like a horse. When I had you I weighed ninety-five pounds. Including you. She doesn't need candles."

"You don't know, Ma." Sol looked intently into his Mother's eyes. "Today Violet slipped in the bathtub."

"Well?"

"She coulda killed herself. As it is, she fainted."

"So you want me to pray because your wife doesn't know how to take a bath. Sol!" Ma waved him away. "Every day millions of people fall down in bathtubs."

"Lissen, Ma," Sol said, holding both her hands. "Nuthin' can't happen to Violet. And nuthin' can happen to the kid. See, Ma? We been tryin' to have a kid for five years now and . . ." he stopped.

Ma shook her head in wonderment. "That big blonde horse."

"We want that kid, Ma. We gotta have that kid. Everybody should have a kid. What've I got if I haven't got a son?"

"Sssh, Baby," Ma said. "Sure, you're right. Only don't yell. You're too nervous to yell."

"All right, I won't yell." Sol wiped the sweat off his forehead with a blue silk handkerchief with a green monogram. "All right. What I want to say is, Violet's dumpin' herself in the bathtub was a omen."

"A what?"

"A omen. It's a. . . ."

"I know."

"It shows us we can't take any chances, Ma."

"Loose in the head, my baby Sol," Ma said. "Too much night life."

"We got to pray to God, Ma," Sol said, "that nuthin' happens to that baby."

"If you want to pray to God, go ahead and pray. Did *I* make the baby?" Ma asked. "Let Violet pray."

Sol swallowed. "Violet's not fit to pray," he said gently. "She's a first-class girl and I would lay down on railroad tracks for her, but she ain't fit to pray to God."

"That's no way to talk about your own wife, Solly," Ma said. "Shame on you."

"I love her like she was my right arm," Sol said. "But she's not a very good woman, Ma. What's the sense in kiddin' ourselves? Violet has a weak character, Ma, and she has done two or three or five things. . . . Give Violet four drinks, Ma, and she says, 'Yes' to the man from Macy's. She's young, she'll outgrow it an' settle down, but right now. . . ." Sol nervously lit a cigarette. "Right now, Ma, Violet's prayers'd carry top weight in the field."

"So, Sol," Ma said gravely, "why can't *you* pray?"

Sol sat quietly, observing his cigarette. The blush came up over his purple collar, like dye soaking in cloth. "I am not one hundred percent perfect in any respect, myself," he said. "First of all, Ma, in my business if yuh don't tell the customers dirty jokes, yuh might just as well apply to the WPA."

"You should've been a doctor, like I said."

"I know, Ma," Sol said patiently. "But I'm not. I'm a man

who has to play in cheap night clubs in Philadelphia and Lowell, Massachusetts, and Boston, weeks at a time. Yuh don't know how lonely it can get at night in Lowell, Massachusetts."

"A lot, Sol?"

"A lot, Ma, a lot." Sol cast his eyes up at the kitchen ceiling.

"A boy with a face like yours." Ma shrugged. "Girls're funny."

"If I prayed, Ma, the words'd stick in my throat."

"So you want me. I don't even believe in God, Baby."

"That's all right, Ma," Sol said. "You're a good woman. Yuh never hurt anybody in all yer life."

Ma sighed hugely. "I'll have to go down to Mrs. Aaronson and get her to teach me the prayer. Sol, darling, you're a nuisance."

Sol kissed her, his eyes shining.

"I got to see what's happening to that bird," Ma said, bending over the chicken. "I'll pray that it's a boy," she said, "while I'm at it."

Every Friday night the candles were lighted and Ma steadfastly said the old words. . . . *"Burach ee, burach shmoi, Burach ee, burach shmoi. Burach ee, burach shmoi. Burach ata adanoi eluchainu melach huoilom. Lehadleck nar shel shabos."* And then she prayed for a boy.

It was on a Friday night that Sol and Violet brought the baby over to Ma's for the first time.

Sol held the boy, smiling and pink and robust as wood in his arms, before his mother.

"See, Ma?" he said, holding the baby out.

Ma put her hand out slowly and gently rubbed the little soft head. "Hair," she said, "he's got hair." She chuckled and took the baby's hand out and kissed it. "Take him into the bedroom, Violet," she said. "I'm busy here for a minute."

She turned and lighted the seven candles in the window, one by one.

"The last stronghold of religion," Lawrence said. "All of a sudden. This house."

"Shut up," Ma said. "City College philosopher."

And she said, *"Burach ee, burach shmoi, Burach ee . . ."* as the candles burned.

AUGUST STRINDBERG

Votive Offering

Vestman of Nedergård Island had been on a schooner trip along the coast of Norway, right up to Lofoten. There he had met some whale-catchers and had learnt one or two things about the art of catching whales with the harpoon. So when he came back to his native isle it occurred to him that he might adapt his newly acquired knowledge to the local method of seal-catching, an industry which was steadily on the decline, owing to the terrifying effect which the noise of the guns had on the timid beasts.

With this object he went to work in the following somewhat ill-advised manner, with a result that neither he nor any one else could have reckoned on, and which gave rise to an adventure of which the story still lives among the skerries.

One evening in late spring Vestman took a boy with him in a flat-bottomed boat to the outer skerries, where the seals used to come ashore to bask in the sun. For the carrying out of this remarkable hunting feat he had brought with him an otter spear, the ordinary purpose of which was the extraction of otters from crevices in the rocks. This weapon, in accordance with the whale-catchers' methods, he had made fast to a windlass in the bows. How he was to get near the timid creatures to catch them with this im-

VOTIVE OFFERING: By August Strindberg from MODERN SWEDISH SHORT STORIES, 1934. Acknowledgments to The Anglo-Swedish Literary Foundation, C.D. Locock, the translator and the publisher, Jonathan Cape Ltd., London.

provised harpoon neither he nor any one else knew; but in case things went wrong his friends said one could always catch fish in a water barrel. But the intended plan of campaign was that the boy should come from the shore side with the gun, while Vestman himself crept along in his boat between the ice-floes and there waited for the flying beasts, which wouldn't be able to move very quickly on the rough drift ice which was heaped up along the short.

Well, he got the boy ashore just before sunset, and started rowing with a pair of woollen stockings twisted round the looms of his oars to deaden the sound, and with a white shirt over his clothes so as to be less conspicuous. And under cover of the rocky islets and pack-ice he managed to row right up to the foot of the slopes, where a gully showed how the beasts had gone up, and how presumably they would have to come down, since there were no holes in the ice.

Vestman sat there, well out of sight, holding aloft the spear at arm's length for such a time that his fingers got frozen and he began to wonder whether the old shot-gun method was not simpler. The seals were there — there was no doubt about that: he heard their cries — but whether they would choose just this risky track for entering the water, that was the great question.

Bang! came the sound from behind the pine-trees on land, and then there was a squeaking in the air and a splashing out at sea, and after that a puffing and a blowing, and then a tapping on the ice like the sound of naked men running along a floor.

Before Vestman had realized how stupid the whole business really was, a shaggy head stuck out through the gap, rose up and plunged into the water, but not before the spear had caught the beast right in the middle. Quick as lightning the rope ran out; the jerk of the boat threw the hunter sprawling over the stern thwarts and off they went at a good round pace for the open sea.

What a lovely ride! Vestman enjoyed the novelty at first, and thought what a splendid hunting story it would make; the booty was already as good as his. But then he saw the boulders dancing past and his own cottage disappear.

"Good-by! So long!" he nodded to the shore. "Back again soon!"

There was jerking and jolting in the boat, but there didn't seem to be any immediate danger till they reached the last rocks and lost sight of land. There was a little sea running, and the sun seemed to have sunk. It looked like a round, black disc on the horizon.

"A bit more," thought Vestman, "and if the worst comes to the worst I shall cut adrift."

So off they went again. But now the boat started rolling, it was meeting the waves and already dipping its nose.

"A little further," thought Vestman. To throw away such a certain catch would be a poor end to such a lovely beginning.

The seas increased and the stars came out. He could still see his axe lying in the bows — his one hope if they went too far.

"On you go, old fellow! You'll soon get tired, if I know you!" muttered the frozen hunter. He was longing to take to the oars and get warm.

At that moment he discovered that his feet were wet and heard the boat's bottom scraping on the rocks.

"Lay off, there!" — the order was to himself — as he got up to cut adrift with the axe. But he promptly sat down again; for just as he was getting up, the seal dragged down the nose of the boat.

After a few unsuccessful attempts to creep forward into the bows he realized the necessity of sitting still; he was at the mercy of the beast, dependent on its whim as to whether he should founder or come home alive.

It was no longer amusing now; a mood of quiet seriousness came over the dispirited hunter. To give himself more courage than he had, he took an oar and stuck it out over the stern, pretending to steer. But he wasn't steering: the beast did that, and always straight out to sea.

"If I ever get out of this, the devil take . . . "

The seal cut a few capers and the oath was broken off; he had to take in the oar and find the bailer to get the water out of the boat.

As soon as he had finished bailing he stuck out the oar again, and at once felt calmer, as though he were really steering.

But by this time the stars had grown dim, and a sprinkle of rain came on, and some snow, so that very soon Vestman could no longer see his axe and found himself completely enveloped in a grey mist. And onward, ever onward, they sped; but the wind seemed on the point of veering, for the seas were now broadside on; and little by little the wind did veer.

And now he began to feel frightened! While he worked the bailer again, he thought of his wife and children, his farm and tools, and then of eternity, which was surely approaching. How he hadn't been to church for — how many years? Well, he couldn't remember, but not since the year of the cholera; and he hadn't been to communion . . . The lee gunwale scraped against the drift ice. "Lord Christ! Poor sinful mortal that I am!" He had forgotten it all . . . "Our Father which art in Heaven . . . Thy will be done as in Heaven . . ." even that!

What long hours, and such a lot of them! A few more and they would be over at Åland, in this wind! But if they came on drift ice they would have to go down with it to Gothland, or into the Gulf of Finland! Before that he would be frozen to death.

He snuggled down into the bottom of the boat to try and get shelter from the icy blast, and as soon as he was on his knees he remembered the whole of the Lord's Prayer and repeated it a score of times; and every time he came to the "Amen" he made a notch in the gunwale with his pocket-knife. And at the sound of his own voice he became calmer; for it seemed as though he were speaking to some one and some one were speaking to him; and the words woke the memory of a crowd of people assembled in church; and he saw them now before him, comforting and reproaching him. He saw there the Gelings, whom he had recently been out with picking up coal from the sunken brig — not quite honest, but perhaps justifiable. He saw there . . . Another jerk of the line! "Lord Jesus, Son of God, if I get out of this alive, I promise, as God lives, a new chandelier with seven candlesticks of pure silver, the whole of my savings for my children — for the church — pure silver! The Lord bless us and keep us; the Lord lift up the light of His countenance upon us and be gracious to us. . . ."

A light shone through the mist, straight ahead; a large light, but dim as a horn lantern.

"It must be Hangö beacon on the Nyland coast," thought Vestman. "I can quite believe we got there in twelve hours; it seemed like a week!"

Another crash under the boat, which stopped dead; Vestman pitched forward over the thwarts, and then all was quiet again.

How far now to the beacon, at a guess? Eight miles! and now he couldn't manage to go either forwards or backwards! It was worse than ever, for the least movement made the boat rock.

Vestman sat still, waiting for sunrise and daylight in the east, while he froze and prayed to God. And he promised and vowed, with every solemn oath, the silver chandelier, hall-marked and costing two hundred dalers, with seven candlesticks and ornaments on the collars; and a chain with balls on it to hang from; and when people saw it they would say, "That is the votive gift of Erik Vestman of Nedergård, whom the Lord helped so graciously in his hour of need, in the year eighteen hundred and fifty-nine!" "God helped him so graciously and mercifully," he kept on repeating, till at last he believed it and in an exuberance of thankfulness for that gracious help recited the opening words of "Glory, praise and thanks to Thee, O Father dear!" God had helped him — that was quite clear, since the chandelier was hanging there, and the people were saying, or rather would say — they hadn't said it yet . . . And now the beacon went out . . . Lord Jesus, who walked upon the water and bade the billows cease! — They ceased now, they had ceased long ago, for it was perfectly smooth; it was really most strange; for here the sea beat with all its might, and just now had been frightful — yesterday evening, since it was now nearly morning — it must be nearly morning when his feet were so frightfully cold and he felt so hungry — he must get some hot coffee soon if only the pilot boat came out, as it must do, since ships would come at sunrise, which had been lying and cruising about the fairway; but why the dev — why in the world had they gone and put out the beacon fire? Perhaps it was daylight, though one couldn't see it on account of the fog; it must be that, unless the Russian Government had some different rules about their beacons; why, probably they had, and now he remembered as if in a dream that the Russians had a different calendar, in the old style — that was the point — thirty days too early or too late — it didn't matter which, for it must be a difference in time; and it *was* too, since the Finnish boats always came in an hour later than the telegraphed time; so that was why they had put out the beacon an hour before sunrise, which was therefore due in an hour. And now he understood why he felt so frightfully cold; everybody who has had the ague feels that at sunrise; but that seal-beast was keeping so quiet and there was no more jerking at the windlass; perhaps it had broken away and gone! He must see about that anyhow! To sit like this unnecessarily — No, dammit!

Vestman looked out ahead and saw something black and spiky like a forest of masts, rising out of the mist.

"Christ! if that's the Russian Fleet they'll shoot me for a smuggler or send me to Siberia. And what a crowd! Holy Father, it's an entire forest!"

He got up and stretched his knees. The boat rocked sideways only; there was no longer any dipping at the bows. Carefully he climbed forward over the thwarts; saw the line stretched tight as a telegraph wire; stepped out of the boat; noticed footprints and struck his heel against a stone . . . he was on land! and there stood a pine wood!

"That you, father?" piped a well-known voice from a juniper shrub.

"Ludwig! What the devil are *you* doing here?"

"I was wondering what had become of you, father!"

Vestman rubbed his eyes: "Tell me — what time is it?"

"Getting on for eight: you've been away the best part of an hour! But I see you've brought the beast back all right!"

The creature lay on the rocks, with the otter spear in its back, dead from loss of blood. It had made a trip out to sea and turned back on account of the swell.

And even to-day that adventure is spoken of as the most

astonishing in the whole history of the skerries except the story of the sea-serpent. And let him that doubts it go to Nedergård Church and look at the little chandelier hanging beneath the organ gallery in everlasting memory of the merciful rescue of one Vestman, formerly crown pilot, from most unusual peril at sea, when with death before his eyes he promised the Lord, for the benefit and edification of the Christian congregation — this tin chandelier.

KATHERINE BRUSH

Good Wednesday

It was a Wednesday. Weekdays in Miss Annie Baxter's life were all pretty much alike; and it might as well have been a Tuesday, or a Thursday, or even a Saturday. But it wasn't — it was a Wednesday. I feel that I should stress this, because Miss Baxter would have. She was herself a storyteller, and the name of the day upon which a thing happened was of tremendous, of vital importance to her. Indeed, her mind sometimes mislaid the anecdote altogether, in the heat of a let-me-see-was-it-a-Thursday-or-was-it-a-Friday debate.

This, then, was a Wednesday. Miss Baxter awoke punctually at six-fifty-nine, and shut off her alarm clock, set for seven. She always beat the clock thus. Only once in a year or more had it roused her. It had been fast. The shock to her nerves had ruined Miss Baxter's whole day.

She got out of bed. She wore a white cotton nightgown with sleeves and a round neck, threaded through and puckered at the throat with blue baby ribbon. She was tall and gaunt in the nightgown, and her bare feet were long and very flat on the floor — they formed capital letter L's with her thin ankles. You were surprised to see that she had slept all night, and apparently perfectly well, with ten or a dozen water-wave combs, bound round with a veil, on her head.

She was not a young woman. She admitted that herself. She said, "I'm forty-three, and I don't make any bones about it" — a proud boast, but inaccurate. She was fifty-one. The hair under the combs was gray and sparse, and Miss Baxter's skin was grayish, and her forehead was deep-grooved from lifting her eyebrows about things. She had sharp, small gray-green eyes, before which she now put shell-rimmed glasses. The rims of the glasses were very light — "champagne-colored" the optician had called them. "Or pale lemon," he had amended hastily, seeing Miss Baxter frown.

Through the glasses she could discern her bedroom slippers — black leather slippers with pompons, although the pompon was off one. A client of Miss Baxter's, one Mrs. Dr. Means, had given her the slippers a year ago Christmas. Putting them on, Miss Baxter thought of Mrs. Dr. Means. She was due to shampoo Mrs. Means to-day at three-thirty, and to cut her, and maybe to dye her. Then again, maybe not. Mrs. Means yearned to be dyed, but was scared of the doctor.

"As if he'd notice!" Miss Baxter scoffed to herself. "He's so begigged with that dish-faced nurse of his, he don't notice *any*thing! I could tell her that." And, indeed, Miss Baxter had all but told Mrs. Means that on several occasions. A hint, she had felt, was the duty of a friend.

This was a cool morning for June. Miss Baxter closed the window — but in much more time than it takes to tell it. She had neighbors, near ones; the windows of the house next door were but a few feet away. Miss Baxter approached her window sideways, along the wall — she sneaked up on it, and flashing out an arm, jerked down the shade. This done, she advanced, reached up underneath with both arms, and lowered the window. It was a breathless moment. She would never forget the day when the shade had suddenly rolled back up of itself, all the way to the top, and left her framed for the world to see in her nightgown.

To-day she had caught an oblique glimpse of something on a window sill next door, and when her own window was shut she applied one eye to a little hole that happened to be in the shade, just about at eye level. She was able to discover that the thing on the opposite sill was a square white florist's box. For some reason this appeared to anger Miss Baxter. She sniffed. It was plain that the sight of the box conveyed more to her than it would have to you or to me, and that she disapproved strongly of the whole business.

While she was dressing the telephone rang. Miss Baxter, over her neat white camisole and petticoat, donned a dressing gown of blue cotton crêpe embroidered with storks — another Christmas present from another customer — and hurried downstairs. The telephone stood on a table in the hall, with an appointment book beside it, and a gayly painted flat wooden doll hiding all but the mouthpiece, which protruded from the doll's green bodice.

Miss Baxter seated herself on the chair beside the telephone. She lifted the receiver delicately and held it to her ear, but she did not say "Hello." She did not say anything. It was not her number that had rung, but the Henry Biddles' number — one long ring and two short. Miss Baxter listened attentively to a conversation between Mrs. Henry Biddle and the milk company. It seemed that the milk company had no whipping cream, but expected to have some later in the day. Mrs. Biddle wanted it by noon. She was promised it by noon, and she and Miss Baxter, in the order named, rang off. Miss Baxter went back upstairs and finished dressing.

She came down again presently, wearing a dark-blue dress with dots in it. A crêpe de Chine dress. It was a matter of pride with her to work in crêpe de Chine dresses. She was no uniformed hairdresser — she was a lady who took care of other ladies' hair. She was as good as anybody in town, and better than most. She wanted this understood, and it was understood and always had been. She was the departed Deacon Baxter's daughter Annie — Miss Baxter to you.

She owned this house she lived in, and she owned a bouncing little car, in which she drove herself from appointment to appointment. She had no "shoppe," no professional parlor, here or anywhere. She carried her implements in a battered leather dressing case, and did her work in her various clients' homes. Sometimes she was asked to stay for a cup of coffee or a bite to eat, or for a meal, if the man of the house was absent. Her clients' husbands were accustomed to avoid Miss Baxter. Miss Baxter said they daren't face her — she knew too much about them.

Arriving for the second time that morning in her lower hall, she unlocked, unchained, and unbolted the front door and opened it. Her copy of the *Daily Herald* lay on the porch, rolled tight and twisted and tossed up there from the sidewalk. She emitted a sound of impatience when she saw it. How many times, she wondered, had she told that little Mooney boy not to roll her paper, and not to twist it, and not to throw it, but to bring it up the steps and lay it down flat like a little man?

She unrolled the paper standing in her doorway, looking up and down the street meanwhile. The street was called Green Street. It was an ordinary thoroughfare lined with unpretentious houses, and with timid maple trees in wire cages, which apparently gave it its name. Miss Baxter, however, found the scenery fascinating. There were the new awnings on the house directly across — those in particular. Miss Baxter had not known that the O'Neills contemplated new awnings, and she had somehow failed to note them when she came home last evening.

They were quite a shock. Miss Baxter's hands on the newspaper stopped, arrested. She stared at the awnings. She counted those she could see. How many awnings were there in all, and what did awnings cost? Whatever they cost, they cost more than Frank O'Neill ought to be spending — owing everybody the way he did. On behalf of Mr. O'Neill's creditors, of whom Miss Baxter was not one, she resented the awnings bitterly.

"Stripes!" she snorted under her breath. She would have been pained to know how like profanity it sounded.

She went in and prepared her breakfast — an orange, some oatmeal, two soft-boiled eggs, toast, marmalade, caffeineless coffee. She set the dining-room table very nicely for herself. You would never catch Miss Annie Baxter eating in the kitchen. She had an electric percolator and an electric toaster from which at intervals the slices of tanned bread sprang forth, making a loud noise about it. Miss Baxter, though she had had this toaster for two years now, always jumped at the noise — though her hand no longer flew to her breast in terror.

She munched, and read the *Herald*, beginning with the society page. This she found unusually meaty and engrossing. Sometimes there wasn't so much, except, of course, the club meetings, and the column called "Brief Mention," in which, in individual two-line paragraphs, were listed all the ladies who had been to Cleveland shopping. Miss Baxter herself, in the past, had twice appeared under "Brief Mention." She had both clippings in an envelope somewhere. One of them said, "Miss Annie Baxter of Green Street was a Cleveland shopper Saturday." The other, of a later date, said, "Among those shopping in Cleveland yesterday was Miss Annie Baxter of Green Street" — only her name was misspelled. It was "Baxten," through some regrettable error.

To-day there was much news. There were shoppers galore, and there were travelers off on trips, and there were convalescent invalids doing well, and there were house guests. Mrs. Archie Weller had entertained a few friends yesterday in honor of her house guest Mrs. S. K. Speare of East Clinton; auction bridge had been enjoyed. The Busy Bees had met with Mrs. Homer Matthews at the latter's beautiful residence on Fairview Boulevard, which was tastefully decorated with daisies and asters. Miss Elsie Corelli of West End, whose marriage to William Sleeper would be celebrated on June 26, had been surprised by her many friends with a tin shower Monday evening. This afternoon Mrs. Henry Biddle would entertain the Hearts and Spades at her pleasant home on Green Street —

"Ah!" thought Miss Baxter. That explained the whipping cream.

Finally, there was a wedding announcement. It was not prominently displayed — it was what the newspaper people call "buried," and what Miss Baxter called "tucked away off down in one corner." She did not see it at all until she had almost finished her breakfast, and her first thought was the appalling one that she might have missed it entirely. This thought came and went. Miss Baxter, tense, was concentrating. She was sitting on the edge of her chair, her face was close to the paper, and both her hands were flattening the page, holding it smooth on the table, so that no slightest wrinkle should come between Miss Baxter and the enlightenment now dawning on her.

What she read was brief. Mrs. Sarah Micou of High Street announced the marriage of her daughter, Annabelle, to James Kendall of Fairview Heights. Unbeknownst to their families or friends, the popular young couple had eloped and been married in Columbus last March —

"I don't believe it!" Miss Baxter cried aloud excitedly.

Since there was no one to hear her, she seemed to feel it unnecessary to explain exactly what it was that she did not believe. She said nothing more aloud, for several minutes. She reread the item many times. An expression almost beatific settled over her countenance — to be supplanted in turn by a crafty, a calculating expression. Miss Baxter raised her eyes from the paper and fixed them, unseeing, on the opposite wall. Her fingers drummed on the table's edge. Or perhaps they counted. Abruptly, triumphantly, Miss Baxter laughed. "December, eh," she said.

She threw the newspaper aside, took a hasty final gulp of coffee, and got up from the table, patting her mouth with her napkin as she rose. At a brisk clip, almost at a canter, she made her way to the telephone, where in the ensuing quarter of an hour she called up half a dozen ladies to ask if they had seen about Annabelle and what they thought.

Four of them had found the item, two by chance and two by direction; and they thought just what Miss Baxter thought. They agreed that it was as plain as the nose on your face. There was no doubt about it. One of them said, indeed, that her sister Isabel had said that Cora Frazee, who worked in the Big Store, in the hat department, had told somebody that one of the customers — Cora wouldn't say who — knew a man who was a clerk at the county courthouse, and that this man, who knew both of them by sight, had with his own two eyes beheld Annabelle and young James Kendall getting a marriage license only last Friday.

Miss Baxter may perhaps be pardoned for her failure to remember quite all the links in this chain of evidence. When she repeated it to Mrs. Dr. Means three minutes later — "I had to call you up, I knew you wouldn't want to wait till this afternoon to hear about it" — Miss Baxter's version was a simplified one. She had the truth, she said, direct from a clerk at the county courthouse, who knew both Annabelle and the Kendall boy very, very well.

"In fact, he used to go with Annabelle himself," Miss Baxter added on a sudden inspiration. "So it looks as if there can't have been any mistake."

An attempt to telephone Cora Frazee was vain. Miss Baxter tried not once, but three or four times. The line was busy. "She's just buzzing about it," Miss Baxter thought acidly.

She forgot Cora Frazee. She made a bold, a dramatic decision. She would call up Mrs. Sarah Micou, the mother of the bride. After all, why not? What could be more natural? Miss Baxter and Mrs. Micou were bosom friends.

"I'll just congratulate her," Miss Baxter thought with a gleam in her eye, "and see what she says."

But there was no answer at the Micous'. Miss Baxter waited a long time, and twice asked if the operator was surely ringing the right number. "Yeah — Micous'," the operator said knowingly, the second time. "I'm ringing 'em all right, but they don't answer."

Thus to the things Miss Baxter could tell you about the Micou-Kendall nuptials was added the fact that Sarah Micou was crushed by the shame and disgrace. She had locked herself into her house. She didn't want to see anybody. She couldn't even bring herself to answer the telephone.

The day had begun well, and it continued better. Mrs. Ed Bletzer of Walnut Street, whose iron-gray boyish bob Miss Baxter treated with oil and washed and "set" from nine until ten-thirty, was most satisfactory. In the first place, she had not heard the news. She hadn't heard a thing. Miss Baxter, still short of breath from mounting the stairs, had to sit right down and give the agog Mrs. Bletzer every last detail before Mrs. Bletzer would suffer her hair to be touched.

"No, no — wait," this client directed, when Miss Baxter tentatively opened her implement case. "Go on. You say they were married yesterday. When? Morning or afternoon?"

"Afternoon," said Miss Baxter, with the conviction of an eyewitness. And indeed, she was rapidly becoming one in her mind.

By the time they got around to the oil treatment, Mrs. Bletzer not only possessed full knowledge of the Micou case — she was able to throw new light on it. Miss Baxter was enthralled to learn that at a recent party Mrs. Bletzer's niece, Ellen, had given, Annabelle Micou had burst into tears for no reason at all. Also, according to Mrs. Bletzer, James Kendall had been trying to borrow money of late. In other words — the unanimous other words of both the ladies — he had been trying, manlike, to skip out of town.

Armed with these colorful additional revelations, Miss Baxter started for Miss Nellie Coe's. Miss Coe, aged fifty, lived with her invalid mother, aged seventy-nine, in half a house on Ohio Avenue. Miss Coe was awaiting Miss Baxter on the porch. "Well, I thought you'd never come!" she called, as Miss Baxter was parking her car. And from old Mrs. Coe's open windows on the second floor issued a hopeful voice, "Is that Annie, Nellie? Tell her to bring her things up here."

"Momma wants me to have the wave in her room," Miss Coe explained. "She wants to hear all about it, too."

Miss Baxter was quite a tease at times. "All about what?" she asked roguishly.

Miss Coe, however, declined to be teased at a time like this. "You know perfectly well about what," she retorted, and hustled Miss Baxter upstairs.

It was at the Coes' that Mrs. Ed Bletzer, all unwitting, was added to the day's feature story, as a humorous touch. "I was at Mrs. Bletzer's before I came here," Miss Baxter related, "and, well, you would have died! Remember her daughter Gertrude, when she was married? That was the summer of twenty-two. No — no, I'm wrong. I beg your pardon. The summer of twenty-three, it was. I remember now. It was the same summer I had my appendix.

Anyway. Where was I? Oh. Well. So here was Mrs. Bletzer asking all about Annabelle, and saying 'Tch! Tch!' and carrying on, pretending to be so shocked — when everybody knows the same thing happened to her own daughter! Well! *Laugh?* I declare, I had all I could do to keep my face straight!"

The Coes snickered appreciatively, and Miss Nellie, who was fond of flapper phraseology, said, "Oh, I *love* that!" Mrs. Coe from her pillows said that that was a good one all right. Miss Baxter, nodding modestly, stood twirling her marceling iron. "It was a scream," she said, to sum it up.

There was a short pause, while their smiles faded. Then Miss Nellie Coe observed thoughtfully, "That was never proved — or proven, I should say — was it? About Gertrude, I mean. I mean she didn't have the baby after all."

"Oh, well, my *dear!*" Miss Baxter said, scornful of this naïveté. "If you want the truth of the matter——"

She lowered her voice and spoke hissingly for some moments.

"I know it for a fact," she said at last aloud.

So that was settled.

Miss Baxter spent so much time upon Miss Coe's marcel, what with letting the irons get too hot while she talked and then cooling them till they were cold, that she was obliged to telephone young Mrs. Billy Lansing and cancel her appointment for quarter of twelve. "Something important has come up," Miss Baxter said. "I can't get there to-day."

She was just as well pleased. Young Mrs. Billy Lansing was uncommunicative. Miss Baxter found this a tiresome characteristic of the young in general. They said "Yes" and "No." They said, "Don't ask me, Miss Baxter, I don't know a thing about it" — when you knew they did. Young Mrs. Billy Lansing, moreover, wasn't even attentive, and what she did listen to she didn't believe. She said, "Oh, that's all birdseed!" Miss Baxter always made short work of her.

Miss Baxter had dinner with Miss Coe. Dinner was at noon in their town. Miss Baxter and Miss Coe dined leisurely from twelve to one-thirty, conversing meanwhile. They had by this time thoroughly covered the chief current topic, but there were sundry secondary topics, and they dealt in these.

It was give and take. Miss Baxter gave this morning's box of flowers on the next-door window sill, which she declared were sent to the youngest Pettingill girl by a married man; and Miss Coe came back with a moonlight swimming party, very scandalous, said to have taken place last Sunday night in Adèle Brierly's pool. Miss Baxter presented a rumor to the effect that Nelson Lansing, who sang in the choir, had had his hair permanent-waved; and Miss Coe supplied a list of the names of those seen petting in parked cars during a recent private dance at the Country Club.

Late developments in the affairs of Dr. Means and the dish-faced nurse were traded by Miss Baxter for a baby Miss Coe predicted and a divorce she practically promised — a fair exchange. Miss Baxter then offered the O'Neills' new awnings, and Miss Coe, much exercised, revealed the fact that the sum of thirty dollars was owed by Frank O'Neill to her brother, Charlie Coe, and had been ever since a poker game last January.

This was more than a fair exchange. Miss Baxter had not known that Charlie Coe played poker. At Mrs. Herbert Jameson's, whither she hastened at quarter of two, she said to Mrs. Jameson that Charlie Coe had taken to gambling "— and carousing," she added smoothly, for the two verbs went together.

"Nellie told me herself," Miss Baxter said, that that might be that. "Just now. I just came from there."

The effect of these tidings upon Mrs. Jameson was unforeseen, and unfortunate. Mrs. Jameson was interested, to be sure; but she was much more. She was anxious, alarmed, upset. It occurred to Miss Baxter belatedly that Charlie Coe was a dentist. He was Mrs. Jameson's dentist, it appeared.

" 'Carousing'?" Mrs. Jameson repeated shrilly. "You mean he *drinks?*"

This was annoying.

"Well, he plays poker," said Miss Baxter. "He gambles. It was the gambling I was thinking of specially."

But it was not the gambling Mrs. Jameson was thinking of

specially. "I don't mind that — that doesn't affect his work," she pointed out, and persisted heatedly, "but he ought not to drink! He ought not to drink a drop! A dentist ought to be sober as a judge!"

"That's true," said Miss Baxter, "but ——"

"Of course it's true! Why, it's only safe and sane! How can he have a steady hand in the morning if he guzzles liquor all night? Oh, dear,"' wailed Mrs. Jameson, "now I'm going to worry myself sick! I'm supposed to go to him first thing to-morrow morning — and what if he's been drunk to-night? I just know he'll pull the wrong tooth or something!"

Miss Baxter during this outburst had twice cleared her throat. She now spoke quickly. "Oh, well, really, I don't know as he drinks as much as all that," she said, and laughed. "He gambles, I know. But maybe he doesn't drink, exactly. Most likely he doesn't drink at all to speak of. I ——"

"But you said he carouses!" Mrs. Jameson had heard Miss Baxter the first time. She had no patience with amendments and revisions. "You're just trying to stick up for him!" she cried accusingly. "You know it's true. Nellie told you herself, didn't she? His own sister ——"

"Well, but maybe she was exaggerating," Miss Baxter suggested. "You know Nellie, how she imagines things."

Mrs. Jameson, however, ignored this.

"His eyes are puffy," she said darkly, "now that I think of it. They're puffy." She thought of another thing, and emitted a triumphant squeak. "And do you know what he did to Mrs. Ives one time? He broke a needle right in her tooth! He said — " Mrs. Jameson put the emphasis where she felt it belonged, " — he *said* it was a defective needle. Hmph! I guess so! A defective dentist is more like it!"

Mrs. Jameson was convinced. Her conviction, though new, was absolute, it was unshakable; and it began to communicate itself to Miss Baxter. The more Mrs. Jameson said — and Mrs. Jameson was voluble — the more clearly Miss Baxter perceived that, after all, she had been right. Intuitively right. It often happened.

She felt much better. Not for anything in the world would Miss Baxter have wronged Charlie Coe, done him professional injury, if he had not deserved it. But a dentist whose dissipations were such that on the mornings-after he broke needles in people's molars, and peered at them with puffy eyes, and tried his best to fit goodness-only-knew-whose gold inlay into Mrs. Jameson's wisdom tooth, as Mrs. Jameson now insisted Charlie once had — that dentist not only deserved, but demanded, exposure. If his practice suffered, it was his own fault. Miss Baxter's conscience troubled her no more.

"After all," she said comfortably, "they all drink like fishes when they play poker. It's part of it."

Mrs. Jameson exclaimed that she guessed you didn't have to tell *her* that! As instance, in passing, she enjoined Miss Baxter to take her neighbor Mr. Anderson: "He plays four and five nights a week somewhere, and comes home late — and I just wish you'd hear him try to get his car in his garage!"

"Wait!" said Miss Baxter tensely. "Let me get this straight. Is it Harry Anderson you're speaking of? Or Arthur?"

"Arthur," grunted Mrs. Jameson.

"Arthur!" exulted Miss Baxter, and thus a new conversational vein was tapped. What Miss Baxter knew about Arthur lasted them until she left.

It was then three-thirty. En route from Mrs. Jameson's to Mrs. Dr. Means's, Miss Baxter thought again of the moral decline of Charlie Coe. She thought, among other things, that she wouldn't have believed it of him — he was such a quiet little man, so meek-appearing. "It just goes to show you, though," Miss Baxter mused. " 'Murder will out,' as I've always——Oh, good heavens!" she protested abruptly aloud. "Have I got a flat tire?"

She had. She had the flattest possible right rear tire. She would have to telephone the garage. For a moment Miss Baxter considered telephoning from her cousin Emily Mason's house, which luckily was very near. On second thought, however, she decided not to bother Emily. She climbed back into the car, and upon the flat tire drove resolutely, though slowly, for perhaps a quarter of a mile — stopping again finally, with an effect of complete breakdown, before a low white house with a green thatched roof. This was the home of a Mr. and Mrs. Warburton, from Chicago. Miss Baxter had always wondered what it was like inside.

Mrs. Warburton was not in, but the local maidservant who opened the door thought it would be all right for Miss Baxter to use the telephone. Miss Baxter called the garage and asked them to come and change the tire. She was a little vague with them, being so preoccupied. Once she absent-mindedly said, "Chinese rug" for "inner tube."

"Bring a new Chinese rug with you," said Miss Baxter.

She proceeded on foot to Mrs. Means's house. The coupé would presently follow. Miss Baxter had lingered long enough to see the garage mechanic arrive, to show him which tire was flat, and to extort from him a promise that, when he had repaired it, he would drive the car along and leave it under Mrs. Means's porte-cochère.

Miss Baxter hurried now. Her implement case banged her speeding knee — though it must be confessed that she did not appear to know it. Her thoughts were elsewhere. To be exact, they were still at the Warburtons'. Miss Baxter was memorizing for future reference a list of items of interest — notable among them a cigarette stub with lipstick at the tip, lying in an ash tray; Mrs. and squat, and had a little hair, mostly gray. She had gray brows, Warburton's bank statement for May, open on a desk; and a black and white crayon drawing, hanging right there on the wall in a frame, of a woman without a stitch on her.

"And children in the house!" Miss Baxter thought, striding along. "Little children! There ought to be a *law.*"

So, in fine fettle, she at last reached Mrs. Means, who all day long had been looking forward to her. Mrs. Means wore a changeable pink-and-lavender taffeta dressing gown, quite new. She would not be shampooed in it, but she wanted Miss Baxter to see it on and tell her frankly whether it suited her. Mrs. Means was short shaped weekly by Miss Baxter with the tweezers and blackened by Mrs. Means when she was going to a bridge party.

Mrs. Means had large and very prominent front teeth, that when she smiled looked somewhat too carnivorous for your comfort. She had eager eyes and was a spellbound listener. She was also an expert finisher of other people's sentences — it did not do to pause for breath when addressing Mrs. Means. She knew, and said, what you were going to say. This irritated some people. It irritated Miss Baxter. "Look here, Harriet!" she would exclaim, "who's telling this?"

They were great cronies. The truth was that Miss Baxter always had more to tell Mrs. Means than there was time for — hence her peevishness at interpolations, however helpfully meant. To-day was no exception. Miss Baxter had so much to tell Mrs. Means that, as she said herself, "I could talk on and on ——"

"All night!" Mrs. Means concluded for her automatically. She emitted an ecstatic chuckle. "Well, *start!*" she commanded, settling herself. "Start with Annabelle Micou."

So Miss Baxter started with Annabelle Micou. . . .

This was at four o'clock. At quarter of six Miss Baxter, still speaking, and Mrs. Means, still listening raptly, emerged together from Mrs. Means's bedroom and descended the staircase to the front door. Miss Baxter was on her way home. "And not only that!" she was saying. "He takes laughing gas in the daytime. Every time he feels the craving coming on him, and he hasn't got a drink around any place, he goes back into that little back office and takes a whiff of laughing gas, and then of course he's drunk as a lord again."

Miss Baxter, then Mrs. Means, passed onto the porch and there halted. It was to be seen that Mrs. Means's eyebrows had been tweezered, for the skin around them looked raw, and that her hair had been shampooed, for obviously you couldn't do a thing with it. It had not been dyed. Again Mrs. Means had lost her courage. She was still afraid of the doctor, she had explained apologetically. She didn't know what on earth the doctor would say.

Miss Baxter had held her temper and her tongue. It was difficult, for Mrs. Means had been vacillating thus for months and months, in a manner to try the patience of a saint. Not only that: to-day was to have been The Day, and Miss Baxter accordingly had promised all previous clients that a treat was in store for them, a spectacle of spectacles — they were to see poor old Harriet Means with her hair dyed black, if they could imagine such a thing.

"Now they'll think I was lying," had been Miss Baxter's aggrieved thought. Her integrity was very precious to her.

Nevertheless, she had controlled herself, she had refrained from giving Mrs. Means the piece of her mind she longed to give her; and no doubt she would have continued to refrain, for the nonce at least, if Mrs. Means, in parting, had not brought it all up again. Mrs. Means was now saying that maybe the next time Miss Baxter came, they would dye the hair. She was once more explaining her timidity heretofore.

"You don't know husbands," she informed Miss Baxter. "You don't know how they are about things."

Miss Baxter's temper snapped quite suddenly.

Mrs. Means continued, "He'd probably kill me —— "

"Nonsense!" Miss Baxter exploded furiously. "For goodness' sake, Harriet, stop being so simple! He *likes* black hair!"

She paused to allow Mrs. Means to remember that the dish-faced nurse's hair was black. Mrs. Means, however, if she remembered, made nothing of it. Her expression was meek and wondering and even hopeful. She seemed on the point of saying, "Do you really think he does?"

Miss Baxter's rage increased. "He wouldn't 'kill' you!" she cried scathingly. "Don't flatter yourself! The chances are he wouldn't even notice your hair was different!" She glowered at Mrs. Means. "Listen!" she commanded, and took a quick breath: "He's got *other things* to think about — I'll tell you *that!*"

The nod with which Miss Baxter punctuated this declaration was impressive. It was a single jerk that must have rattled the teeth in her head. She wheeled then and tramped down the four porch steps. "I may not know husbands," she shot back over her shoulder at the blinking Mrs. Means, "but I know *that!*"

The coupé stood at the foot of the steps, under the porte-cochère. It quivered and creaked with Miss Baxter's climbing in. She slammed the door and rattled the keys that hung on a chain from the switch. She looked through the window. Mrs. Means at the top of the steps was still staring at her.

"Well, good-bye," Miss Baxter said sardonically.

She started the engine. She had her hand on the brake, releasing it, when Mrs. Means abruptly called out, "Wait! Wait just a minute!"

Miss Baxter waited. Mrs. Means hurried down the steps and confronted the window. She seized the frame with her hands. She was troubled now, Miss Baxter saw. Her eyes were uneasy, fearful, under the reddened, slightly swollen brows.

"Annie," she said. "What do you mean? What 'other things'?"

Miss Baxter regarded her thoughtfully.

"You mean his practice, don't you?" Mrs. Means said, on a pleading note. "His work. That's what you mean, isn't it?"

Miss Baxter's wrath had abated, evidently. She smiled, and her answering voice was gentle. "Why, of course, Harriet," she said. "What else would I mean? His work at the hospital, and his office hours, and his outside patients—and all the time he spends with his nurse. . . . Those things keep him busy," Miss Baxter finished blandly. "He's a busy man. That's all I meant."

She put her car in gear. "I've got to run along now, dear," she said. "It's almost supper time."

She left Mrs. Means to think it over.

Miss Baxter was tired when she got home. It had been a busy day. All days were busy except the Sabbath, and she was always tired at supper time. She did not mind. This was a good, a peaceful weariness. It was contentment. "Something accomplished, something done."

She prepared a casual meal of tea and salad and sardines, and bread and butter, and ate it slowly, restfully, in the quiet dining room. She sat there long, in pleasant reverie.

The clock on the dining-room mantel, striking, roused her.

Seven o'clock. "Here!" Miss Baxter said aloud. She jumped up briskly. "I'd better get a move on. I'll be late."

She folded her napkin and rolled it and slipped it into the silver ring marked "Annie" that she had had since she was five. She cleared the table hurriedly and crumbed it with her hands, bearing the crumbs in one palm to the window sill. "There, little birds," she said. She put the butter in the icebox, and the napkin and the sugar bowl on the sideboard. She did not wash the dishes. What few there were could wait.

All this took but a moment. Miss Baxter rinsed her hands and dried them and left the kitchen, passing through the dining room to the parlor. Here there was an immense black desk that had been her father's, wide as the opposite sofa, high as the windows.

Miss Baxter opened the desk, revealing pigeonholes neat with papers. She pulled up a straight chair and sat on the edge of it. There was not much time, but she had a little note to write. A note to Annabelle Micou, the bride.

She addressed the envelope first. She did not write the address, but printed it, in black ink on a plain stamped envelope. "Mrs. James Kendall, care Mrs. Sarah Micou, High Street, City." She looked at it carefully. It looked all right. Wouldn't it be better, though, to misspell "Micou" somehow — say, to put a "k" after the "c"?

She believed it would be better. She destroyed the first attempt, tearing it to atoms, and took out another plain stamped envelope and tried again. This time she was satisfied. They would never guess now. She put the envelope aside to dry.

She printed the note as well. Miss Baxter was an experienced printer. She could make the letters straight and schooled, or crude and sprawling. These were sprawling. There were three short lines, that, for all their brevity, almost covered a piece of blue-ruled composition paper. There were two words to the first line, two to the second, two to the third. "THE WAGES — OF SIN — IS DEATH!" the note read, and the final word was huge and black and underscored heavily to the foot of the page.

Miss Baxter added more exclamation points, and a signature.

The signature gave her some trouble. "One Who Knows" would not quite do. She nibbled the end of her pen for a moment, and then printed simply, "A Friend."

On the whole, she was pleased with the note. The message was one she had sent sometimes before to people who needed it, but never before to Annabelle Micou. " 'The wages of sin is death,' " Miss Baxter repeated sonorously, folding the letter. Her voice had gusto, but her eyebrows drew together in a frown. Why "is"? Why not, "The wages *are*"? That always worried her.

She sealed the letter and closed the desk again. It was quarter-past seven now by the clock in the hall. Miss Baxter rushed up the staircase, leaving the letter on the newel post where she would not fail to see it and take it along with her to mail. Annabelle should have it first thing in the morning.

She was upstairs but a very short time, during which her rapid footsteps circulated overhead. She reappeared wearing a ladylike lavender hat and a white silk dress, and clutching a small black book with gilt-edged leaves and a cross on the cover, and a sealed manila envelope containing a contribution. To this handful she added the letter from the newel post as she passed. Her free hand wrenched the knob of the front door. . . .

Miss Baxter was bound for prayer meeting, for this was Wednesday evening. Tired as she was from her strenuous day, she could not have remained at home. Miss Baxter was very devout. She always had been. "Other people," she often said, "can stay away from divine worship. But I don't know *how* they can! *I* couldn't — and feel right with God."

SALLY BENSON

The Overcoat

It had been noisy and crowded at the Milligan's and Mrs. Bishop had eaten too many little sandwiches and too many iced cakes, so that now, out in the street, the air felt good to her, even if it was damp and cold. At the entrance of the apartment house, she took out her change purse and looked through it and found that by counting the pennies, too, she had just eighty-seven cents, which wasn't enough for a taxi from Tenth Street to Seventy-Third. It was horrid never having enough money in your purse, she thought. Playing bridge, when she lost, she often had to give IOU's and it was faintly embarrassing, although she always managed to make them good. She resented Lila Hardy who could say, "Can anyone change a ten?" and who could take ten dollars from her smart bag while the others scurried for change.

She decided it was too late to take a bus and that she might as well walk over to the subway, although the air down there would probably make her head ache. It was drizzling a little and the sidewalks were wet. And as she stood on the corner waiting for the traffic lights to change, she felt horribly sorry for herself. She remembered as a young girl, she had always assumed she would have lots of money when she was older. She had planned what to do with it — what clothes to buy and what upholstery she would

---

THE OVERCOAT: By Sally Benson from AMERICAN MERCURY, 1934. American Mercury, P.O. Box 1306, Torrance, California 90505.

have in her car. Of course, everybody nowadays talked poor and that was a comfort. But it was one thing to have lost your money and quite another never to have had any. It was absurd, though, to go around with less than a dollar in your purse. Suppose something happened? She was a little vague as to what might happen, but the idea fed her resentment.

Everything for the house, like food and things, she charged. Years ago, Robert had worked out some sort of budget for her but it had been impossible to keep their expenses under the right headings, so they had long ago abandoned it. And yet Robert always seemed to have money. That is, when she came to him for five or ten dollars, he managed to give it to her. Men were like that, she thought. They managed to keep money in their pockets but they had no idea you ever needed any. Well, one thing was sure, she would insist on having an allowance. Then she would know where she stood. When she decided this, she began to walk more briskly and everything seemed simpler.

The air in the subway was worse than usual and she stood on the local side waiting for a train. People who took the express seemed to push so and she felt tired and wanted to sit down. When the train came, she took a seat near the door and, although inwardly she was seething with rebellion, her face took on the vacuous look of other faces in the subway. At Eighteenth Street, a great many people got on and she found her vision blocked by a man who had come in and was hanging to the strap in front of her. He was tall and thin and his overcoat which hung loosely on him and swayed with the motion of the train smelled unpleasantly of damp wool. The buttons of the overcoat were of imitation leather and the button directly in front of Mrs. Bishop's eyes evidently had come off and been sewed back on again with black thread, which didn't match the coat at all.

It was what is known as a swagger coat but there was nothing very swagger about it now. The sleeve that she could see was almost threadbare around the cuff and a small shred from the lining hung down over the man's hand. She found herself looking intently at his hand. It was long and pallid and not too clean. The nails were very short as though they had been bitten and there was a discolored callus on his second finger where he probably held his pencil. Mrs. Bishop, who prided herself on her powers of observation, put him in the white-collar class. He most likely, she thought, was the father of a large family and had a hard time sending them all through school. He undoubtedly never spent money on himself. That would account for the shabbiness of his overcoat. And he was probably horribly afraid of losing his job. Mrs. Bishop couldn't decide whether to make his wife a fat slattern or to have her an invalid.

She grew warm with sympathy for the man. Every now and then he gave a slight cough, and that increased her interest and her sadness and made her feel resigned to life. She decided that she would smile at him when she got off. It would be the sort of smile that would make him feel better, as it would be very obvious that she understood and was sorry.

But by the time the train reached Seventy-Second Street, the closeness of the air and the confusion of her own worries had made her feelings less poignant, so that her smile, when she gave it, lacked something. The man looked away embarrassed.

Her apartment was too hot and the smell of broiling chops sickened her after the enormous tea she had eaten. She could see Maude, her maid, setting the table in the dining room for dinner. Mrs. Bishop had bought smart little uniforms for her, but there was nothing smart about Maude and the uniforms never looked right.

Robert was lying on the living room couch, the evening newspaper over his face to shield his eyes. He had changed his shoes, and the gray felt slippers he wore were too short for him and showed the imprint of his toes, and looked depressing. Years ago, when they were first married, he used to dress for dinner sometimes. He would shake up a cocktail for her and things were quite gay and almost the way she had imagined they would be. Mrs. Bishop didn't believe in letting yourself go and it seemed to her that Robert let himself go out of sheer perversity. She hated him as he lay there, resignation in every line of his body. She envied

Lila Hardy her husband who drank but who, at least, was somebody. And she felt like tearing the newspaper from his face because her anger and disgust were more than she could bear.

For a minute she stood in the doorway trying to control herself and then she walked over to a window and opened it roughly. "Goodness," she said. "Can't we ever have any air in here?"

Robert gave a slight start and sat up. "Hello, Mollie," he said. "You home?"

"Yes, I'm home," she answered. "I came home in the subway."

Her voice was reproachful. She sat down in the chair facing him and spoke more quietly so that Maude couldn't hear what she was saying. "Really, Robert," she said, "it was dreadful. I came out from the tea in all that drizzle and couldn't even take a taxi home. I had exactly eighty-seven cents!"

"Say," he said. "That's a shame. Here." He reached in his pocket and took out a small roll of crumpled bills. "Here," he repeated. And handed her one. She saw that it was five dollars.

Mrs. Bishop shook her head. "No, Robert," she told him. "That isn't the point. The point is that I've really got to have some sort of allowance. It isn't fair to me. I never have any money! Never! It's got so it's positively embarrassing!"

Mr. Bishop fingered the five-dollar bill thoughtfully. "I see," he said. "You want an allowance. Don't I give you money every time you ask for it?"

"Well, yes," Mrs. Bishop admitted. "But it isn't like my own. An allowance would be more like my own."

"Now, Mollie," he reasoned. "If you had an allowance, it would probably be gone by the tenth of the month."

"Don't treat me like a child," she said. "I just won't be humiliated any more."

Mr. Bishop sat turning the five-dollar bill over and over in his hand. "How much do you think you should have?"

"Fifty dollars a month," she told him. And her voice was harsh. "That's the least I can get along on. Why, Lila Hardy would laugh at fifty dollars a month."

"Fifty dollars a month," Mr. Bishop repeated. He ran his

fingers through his hair. "I've had a lot of things to attend to this month. But, well, maybe if you would be willing to wait until the first of next month, I might manage."

"Oh, next month will be perfectly all right," she said, feeling it wiser not to press her victory. "But don't forget all about it. Because I shan't."

As she walked toward the closet to put away her wraps, she caught sight of Robert's overcoat on the chair near the door. He had tossed it carelessly across the back of the chair as he came in. One sleeve was hanging down and the vibration of her feet on the floor had made it swing gently back and forth. She saw that the cuff was badly worn and a bit of the lining showed. It looked dreadfully like the sleeve of the overcoat she had seen in the subway. And, suddenly, looking at it, she had a horrible sinking feeling, as though she were falling in a dream.

WILBUR DANIEL STEELE

The Man Who Saw Through Heaven

People have wondered (there being obviously no question of romance involved) how I could ever have allowed myself to be let in for the East African adventure of Mrs. Diana in search of her husband. There were several reasons. To begin with, the time and effort and money weren't mine; they were the property of the wheel of which I was but a cog, the Society through which Diana's life had been insured, along with the rest of that job-lot of missionaries. The "letting in" was the firm's. In the second place, the wonderers have not counted on Mrs. Diana's capacity for getting things done for her. Meek and helpless. Yes, but God was on her side. Too meek, too helpless to move mountains herself, if those who happened to be handy didn't move them for her then her God would know the reason why. Having dedicated her all to making straight the Way, why should her neighbour cavil at giving a little? The writer for one, a colonial governor general for another, railway magnates, insurance managers, *safari* leaders, the ostrich-farmer of Ndua, all these and a dozen others in their turn have felt the hundred-ton weight of her thin-lipped meekness — have seen her in metaphor sitting grimly on the doorsteps of their souls.

A third reason lay in my own troubled conscience. Though I did it in innocence, I can never forget that it was I who personally conducted Diana's party to the Observatory on that fatal night in Boston before it sailed. Had it not been for that kindly intentioned "hunch" of mine, the astounded eye of the Reverend Hubert Diana would never have gazed through the floor of Heaven, and he would never have undertaken to measure the Infinite with the foot-rule of his mind.

It all started so simply. My boss at the shipping-and-insurance office gave me the word in the morning. "Bunch of missionaries for the *Platonic* to-morrow. They're on our hands in a way. Show 'em the town." It wasn't so easy when you think of it: one male and seven females on their way to the heathen; though it was easier in Boston than it might have been in some other towns. The evening looked the simplest. My friend Krum was at the Observatory that semester; there at least I was sure their sensibilities would come to no harm.

On the way out in the streetcar, seated opposite to Diana and having to make conversation, I talked of Krum and of what I knew of his work with the spiral nebulae. Having to appear to listen, Diana did so (as all day long) with a vaguely indulgent smile. He really hadn't time for me. That night his life was exalted as it had never been, and would perhaps never be again. To-morrow's sailing, the actual fact of leaving all to follow Him, held his imagination in thrall. Moreover, he was a bridegroom of three days with his bride beside him, his nerves at once assuaged and thrilled. No, but more. As if a bride were not enough, arrived in Boston, he had found himself surrounded by a very galaxy of womanhood gathered from the four corners; already within hours one felt the chaste tentacles of their feminine dependence curling about the party's unique man; already their contacts with the world of their new lives began to be made through him; already they saw in part through his eyes. I wonder what he would have said if I had told him he was a little drunk.

In the course of the day I think I had got him fairly well. As concerned his Church he was at once an asset and a liability. He believed its dogma as few still did, with a simplicity, "the old-time religion." He was born that kind. Of the stuff of the fanatic, the reason he was not a fanatic was that, curiously impervious to little questionings, he had never been aware that his faith was anywhere attacked. A self-educated man, he had accepted the necessary smattering facts of science with a serene indulgence, as simply so much further proof of what the Creator could do when He put His Hand to it. Nor was he conscious of any conflict between these facts and the fact that there existed a substantial Heaven, geographically up, and a substantial Hot Place, geographically down.

So, for his Church, he was an asset in these days. And so, and for the same reason, he was a liability. The Church must after all keep abreast of the times. For home consumption, with modern congregations, especially urban ones, a certain streak of "healthy" skepticism is no longer amiss in the pulpit; it makes people who read at all more comfortable in their pews. A man like Hubert Diana is more for the cause than a hundred. But what to do with him? Well, such things arrange themselves. There's the Foreign Field. The blacker the heathen the whiter the light they'll want, and the solider the conception of a God the Father enthroned in a Heaven of which the sky above them is the visible floor.

And that, at bottom, was what Hubert Diana believed. Accept as he would with the top of his brain the fact of a spherical earth zooming through space, deep in his heart he knew that the world lay flat from modern Illinois to ancient Palestine, and that the sky above it, blue by day and by night festooned with guiding stars for wise men, was the nether side of a floor on which the resurrected trod. . . .

I shall never forget the expression of his face when he realized he was looking straight through it that night. In the quiet dark of the dome I saw him remove his eye from the eye-piece of the telescope up there on the staging and turn it in the ray of a hooded bulb on the demon's keeper, Krum.

"What's that, Mr. Krum? I didn't get you!"

"I say, that particular cluster you're looking at —"

"This star, you mean?"

"You'd have to count awhile to count the stars describing their orbits in that 'star,' Mr. Diana. But what I was saying — have you ever had the wish I used to have as a boy — that you could actually look back into the past? With your own two eyes?"

Diana spoke slowly. He didn't know it, but it had already begun to happen; he was already caught. "I have often wished, Mr. Krum, that I might actually look back into the time of our Lord. Actually. Yes."

Krum grunted. He was young. "We'd have to pick a nearer neighbor than *Messier 79* then. The event you see when you put your eye to that lens is happening much too far in the past. The light-waves thrown off by that particular cluster on the day, say, of the Crucifixion — *you* won't live to see them. They've hardly started yet — a mere twenty centuries on their way — leaving them something like eight hundred and thirty centuries yet to come before they reach the earth."

Diana laughed the queerest catch of a laugh. "And — and there — there won't be any earth here, then, to welcome them."

"What?" It was Krum's turn to look startled. So for a moment the two faces remained in confrontation, the one, as I say, startled, the other exuding visibly little seagreen globules of sweat. It was Diana that caved in first, his voice hardly louder than a whisper. "W-w-will there?"

None of us suspected the enormousness of the thing that had happened in Diana's brain. Krum shrugged his shoulders and snapped his fingers. Deliberately. *Snap!* "What's a thousand centuries or so in the cosmic reckoning?" He chuckled. "We're just beginning to get out among 'em with *Messier*, you know. In the print room, Mr. Diana, I can show you photographs of clusters to which, if you cared to go, travelling at the speed of light ——"

The voice ran on; but Diana's eye had gone back to the eye-piece, and his affrighted soul had reentered the big black tube sticking its snout out of the slit in the iron hemisphere. . . . "At the speed of light!" . . . That unsuspected, that wildly chance-found chink in the armour of his philosophy! The body is resurrected and it ascends to Heaven instantaneously. At what speed must it be borne to reach instantaneously that city beyond the ceiling of the sky? At a speed inconceivable, mystical. At, say (as he had often said to himself), *the speed of light. . . .* And now, hunched there in the trap that had caught him, black rods, infernal levers and wheels, he was aware of his own eye passing vividly through unpartitioned emptiness, *eight hundred and fifty centuries at the speed of light!*

"And still beyond these," Krum was heard, "we begin to come into the regions of the spiral nebulae. We've some interesting photographs in the print room, if you've the time."

The ladies below were tired of waiting. One had "lots of packing to do." The bride said, "Yes, I do think we should be getting along. Hubert, dear, if you're ready ——"

The fellow actually jumped. It's lucky he didn't break anything. His face looked greener and dewier than ever amid the contraptions above. "If you — you and the ladies, Cora — wouldn't mind — if Mr. — Mr. — (he'd mislaid my name) would see you back to the hotel ——" Meeting silence, he began to expostulate. "I feel that this is a rich experience. I'll follow shortly; I know the way."

In the car going back into the city Mrs. Diana set at rest the fluttering of six hearts. Being unmarried, they couldn't understand men as she did. When I think of that face of hers, to which I was destined to grow only too accustomed in the weary, itchy days of the trek into Kavirondoland, with its slightly tilted nose, its irregular pigmentation, its easily inflamed lids, and long moist cheeks, like a hunting dog, glorying in weariness, it seems incredible that a light of coyness could have found lodgment there. But that night it did. She sat serene among her virgins.

"You don't know Bert. You wait; he'll get a perfectly wonderful sermon out of all that to-night, Bert will."

Krum was having a grand time with his neophyte. He would have stayed up all night. Immured in the little print room crowded with files and redolent of acids, he conducted his disciple "glassy-eyed" through the dim frontiers of space, holding before him one after another the likenesses of universes sister to our own, islanded in immeasurable vacancy, curled like glimmering crullers on their private Milky Ways, and hiding in their wombs their myriad "coal-pockets," star-dust foetuses of which — their quadrillion years accomplished — their litters of new suns would be born, to bear their planets, to bear their moons in turn.

"And beyond these?"

Always after each new feat of distance, it was the same. "And beyond?" Given an ell, Diana surrendered to a pop-eyed lust for nothing less than light-years. "And still beyond?"

"Who knows?"

"The mind quits. For if there's no end to these nebulae —— "

"But supposing there is?"

"An end? But, Mr. Krum, in the very idea of an ending —— "

"An end to what we might call this particular category of magnitudes. Eh?"

"I don't get that."

"Well, take this — take the opal in your ring there. The numbers and distances inside that stone may conceivably be to themselves as staggering as ours to us in our own system. Come! that's not so far-fetched. What are we learning about the structure of the atom? A nucleus (call it a sun) revolved about in eternal orbits by electrons (call them planets, worlds). Infinitesimal; but after all, what are bigness and littleness but matters of comparison? To eyes on one of those electrons (don't be too sure there aren't any) its tutelary sun may flame its way across a heaven a comparative ninety million miles away. Impossible for them to conceive of a boundary to their billions of atomic systems, molecular universes. In that category of magnitudes its diameter is infinity; once it has made the leap into our category and become an opal it is merely a quarter of an inch. That's right, Mr. Diana, you may well stare at it: between *now* and *now* ten thousand histories may have come and gone down there. . . . And just so the diameter of our own cluster of universes, going over into another category, may be —— "

"May be a — a ring — a little stone — in a — a — a — ring."

Krum was tickled by the way the man's imagination jumped and engulfed it.

"Why not? That's as good a guess as the next. A ring, let's say, worn carelessly on the — well, say the tentacle — of some vast organism—some inchoate creature hobnobbing with its cloudy kind in another system of universes — which in turn ——"

It is curious that none of them realized next day that they were dealing with a stranger, a changed man. Why he carried on, why he capped that night of cosmic debauch by shaving, eating an unremarkable breakfast, packing his terrestrial toothbrush and collars, and going up the gangplank in tow of his excited convoy to sail away, is beyond explanation — unless it was simply that he was in a daze.

It wasn't until four years later that I was allowed to know what had happened on that ship, and even then the tale was so disjointed, warped, and opinionated, so darkly seen in the mirror of Mrs. Diana's orthodoxy, that I had almost to guess what it was *really* all about.

"When Hubert turned irreligious. . . ." That phrase, recurrent on her tongue in the meanderings of the East Africa quest to which we were by then committed, will serve to measure her understanding. Irreligious! Good Lord! But from that sort of thing I had to reconstruct the drama. Evening after evening beside her camp fire (appended to the Mineral Survey Expedition Toward Uganda through the kindness — actually the worn-down surrender — of the Protectorate government) I lingered awhile before joining the merrier engineers, watched with fascination the bumps growing under the mosquitoes on her forehead, and listened to the jargon of her mortified meekness and her scandalized faith.

There had been a fatal circumstance, it seems, at the very outset. If Diana could but have been seasick, as the rest of them were (horribly), all might still have been well. In the misery of desired death, along with the other contents of a heaving midriff, he might have brought up the assorted universes of which he had been led too rashly to partake. But he wasn't. As if his wife's theory was right, as if Satan was looking out for him, he was spared to prowl the swooping decks immune. Four days and nights alone. Time enough to digest and assimilate into his being beyond remedy that lump of whirling magnitudes and to feel himself surrendering with a strange new ecstasy to the drunkenness of liberty.

Such liberty! Given Diana's type, it is hard to imagine it adequately. The abrupt, complete removal of the toils of reward and punishment; the withdrawal of the surveillance of an all-seeing, all-knowing Eye; the windy assurance of being responsible for nothing, important to no one, no longer (as the police say) "wanted"! It must have been beautiful in those few days of its first purity, before it began to be discoloured by his contemptuous pity for others, the mask of his inevitable loneliness and his growing fright.

The first any of them knew of it — even his wife — was in mid-voyage, the day the sea went down and the seven who had been sick came up. There seemed an especial Providence in the calming of the waters; it was Sunday morning and Diana had been asked to conduct the services.

He preached on the text: "For such is the kingdom of Heaven."

"If our concept of God means anything it means a God *all*-mighty, Creator of *all* that exists, Director of the *infinite*, cherishing in His Heaven the saved souls of *all space and all time*."

Of course; amen. And wasn't it nice to feel like humans again, and real sunshine pouring up through the lounge ports from an ocean suddenly grown kind. . . . But — then — *what* was Diana *saying?*

Mrs. Diana couldn't tell about it coherently even after a lapse of fifty months. Even in a setting as remote from that steamer's lounge as the equatorial bush, the ember-reddened canopy of thorn trees, the meandering camp fires, the chant and tramp somewhere away of Kikuyu porters dancing in honour of an especial largesse of fat zebra meat — even here her memory of that impious outburst was too vivid, too aghast.

"It was Hubert's look! The way he stared at us! As if you'd said he was licking his chops! . . . That *'Heaven'* of his!"

It seems they hadn't waked up to what he was about until he had the dimensions of his sardonic Paradise irreparably drawn in. The final haven of all right souls. Not alone the souls released from this our own tiny earth. In the millions of solar systems we see as stars how many millions of satellites must there be upon which at some time in their histories conditions suited to organic life subsist? Uncounted hordes of wheeling populations! Of men? God's creatures at all events, a portion of them reasoning. Weirdly shaped, perhaps, but what of that? And that's only to speak of our own inconsiderable cluster of universes. That's to say nothing of other systems of magnitudes, where God's creatures are to our world what we are to the world's in the atoms in our finger rings. (He had shaken *his,* here, in their astounded faces.) And all these, all the generations of these enormous and microscopic beings harvested through a time beside which the life-span of our earth is as a second in a million centuries: all these brought to rest for an eternity to which time itself is a watch-tick — all crowded to rest pell-mell, thronged, serried, packed, packed to suffocation in layers unnumbered light-years deep. This must needs be our concept of Heaven if God is God of the Whole. If, on the other hand ——

The other hand was the hand of the second officer, the captain's delegate at divine worship that Sabbath day. He at last had "come to."

I don't know whether it was the same day or the next; Mrs. Diana was too vague. But here's the picture. Seven women huddled in the large stateroom on B-deck, conferring in whispers, aghast, searching one another's eyes obliquely even as they bowed their heads in prayer for some light — and of a sudden the putting back of the door and the in-marching of the Reverend Hubert. . . .

As Mrs. Diana tried to tell me, "You understand, don't you, he had just taken a bath? And he hadn't—he had forgotten to——"

Adam-innocent there he stood. Not a stitch. But I don't believe for a minute it was a matter of forgetting. In the high intoxication of his soul-release, already crossed (by the second officer) and beginning to show his zealot claws, he needed some gesture stunning enough to witness to his separation, his unique rightness, his contempt of match-flare civilizations and infinitesimal taboos.

But I can imagine that stateroom scene: the gasps, the heads colliding in aversion, and Diana's six weedy feet of birthday-suit towering in the shadows, and ready to sink through the deck, I'll warrant, now the act was irrevocable, but still grimly carrying it off.

"And if, on the other hand, you ask me to bow down before a God peculiar to this one earth, this one grain of dust lost among the giants of space, watching its sparrows fall, profoundly interested in a speck called Palestine no bigger than the quadrillionth part of one of the atoms in the ring here on my finger ——"

Really scared by this time, one of the virgins shrieked. It was altogether too close quarters with a madman.

Mad? Of course there was the presumption: "Crazy as a loon." Even legally it was so adjudged at the *Platonic's* first port-of-call, Algiers, where, when Diana escaped ashore and wouldn't come back again, he had to be given over to the workings of the French law. I talked with the magistrate myself some forty months later, when, "let in" for the business as I have told, I stopped there on my way out.

"But what would you?" were his words. "We must live in the world as the world lives, is it not? Sanity? Sanity is what? Is it, for example, an intellectual clarity, a balanced perception of the realities? Naturally, speaking out of court, your friend was of a sanity—of a sanity, sir——" Here the magistrate made with thumb and fingers the gesture only the French can make for a thing that is matchless, a beauty, a transcendent instance of any kind. He himself was Gallic, rational. Then, with a lift of shoulder, "But what would you? We must live in the world that seems."

Diana, impounded in Algiers for deportation, escaped. What, after all, are the locks and keys of this pinchbeck category of magnitudes? More remarkable still, there in Arab Africa, he succeeded in vanishing from the knowledge and pursuit of men. And of women. His bride, now that their particular mission had fallen through, was left to decide whether to return to America or to go on with two of the company, the Misses Brookhart and Smutts, who were bound for a school in Smyrna. In the end she followed the latter course. It was there, nearly four years later, that I was sent to join her by an exasperated and worn-out Firm.

By that time she knew again where her husband-errant was—

or where at least, from time to time in his starry dartings over this our mote of dust, he had been heard of, spoken to, seen.

Could we but have a written history of those years of his apostolic vagabondage, a record of the towns in which he was jailed or from which he was kicked out, of the ports in which he starved, of the ships on which he stowed away, presently to reveal himself in proselyting ardour, denouncing the earthlings, the fatelings, the dupes of bugaboo, meeting scoff with scoff, preaching the new revelation red-eyed, like an angry prophet. Or was it, more simply, like a man afraid?

Was that the secret, after all, of his prodigious restlessness? Had it anything in common with the swarming of those pale worms that flee the Eye of the Infinite around the curves of the stone you pick up in a field? Talk of the man without a country! What of the man without a universe?

It is curious that I never suspected his soul's dilemma until I saw the first of his mud-sculptures in the native village of Ndua in the province of Kasuma in British East. Here it was, our objective attained, we parted company with the government *safari* and shifted the burden of Way-straightening to the shoulders of Major Wyeside, the ostrich-farmer of the neighborhood.

While still on the *safari* I had put to Mrs. Diana a question that had bothered me: "Why on earth should your husband ever have chosen this particular neck of the woods to land up in? Why Kavirondoland?"

"It was here we were coming at the time Hubert turned irreligious, to found a mission. It's a coincidence, isn't it?"

And yet I would have sworn Diana hadn't a sense of humour about him anywhere. But perhaps it *wasn't* an ironic act. Perhaps it was simply that, giving up the struggle with a society blinded by "a little learning" and casting about for a virgin field, he had remembered this.

"I supposed he was a missionary," Major Wyeside told us with a flavour of indignation. "I went on that. I let him live here — six or seven months of it — while he was learning the tongue.

I was a bit nonplussed, to put it mildly, when I discovered what he was up to."

What things Diana had been up to the Major showed us in one of the huts in the native kraal — a round dozen of them, modelled in mud and baked. Blackened blobs of mud, that's all. Likenesses of nothing under the sun, fortuitous masses sprouting haphazard tentacles, only two among them showing pustules that might have been experimental heads. . . . The ostrich-farmer saw our faces.

"Rum, eh? Of course I realized the chap was anything but fit. A walking skeleton. Nevertheless, whatever it is about these beasties, there's not a nigger in the village has dared set foot inside this hut since Diana left. You can see for yourselves it's about to crash. There's another like it he left at Suki, above here. Taboo, no end!"

So Diana's "hunch" had been right. He had found his virgin field indeed, fit soil for his cosmic fright. A religion in the making, here before our eyes.

"This was at the very last before he left," Wyeside explained. "He took to making these mud-pies quite of a sudden; the whole lot within a fortnight's time. Before that he had simply talked, harangued. He would sit here in the doorway of an evening with the niggers squatted around and harangue 'em by the hour. I knew something of it through my house-boys. The most amazing rot. All about the stars to begin with, as if these black baboons could half grasp *astronomy!* But that seemed all proper. Then there was talk about a something a hundred times as big and powerful as the world, sun, moon, and stars put together — some perfectly enormous stupendous awful being — but knowing how mixed the boys can get, it still seemed all regular — simply the parson's way of getting at the notion of an Almighty God. But no, they insisted, there wasn't any God. That's the point, they said; there *is no* God. . . . Well, that impressed me as a go. That's when I decided to come down and get the rights of this star-swallowing monstrosity the beggar was feeding my labour on. And here he sat in the door way with one of these beasties — here it is, this one — waving it furiously in the niggers' benighted faces. And do you know what he'd done? — you can see the mark here still on this wabble-leg, this tentacle-business — he had taken off a ring he had and screwed it on just here. His finger ring, my word of honour! And still, if you'll believe it, I didn't realize he was just daft. Not until he spoke to me. 'I find,' he was good enough to enlighten me, 'I find I have to make it somehow concrete.' . . . 'Make what?' . . . 'Our wearer.' . . . 'Our *what, where?*' . . . 'In the following category.' . . . His actual words, honour bright. I was going to have him sent down-country where he could be looked after. He got ahead of me though. He cleared out. When I heard he'd turned up at Suki I ought, I suppose, to have attended to it. But I was having trouble with leopards. And you know how things go."

From there we went to Suki, the Major accompanying. It was as like Ndua as one flea to its brother, a stockade inclosing round houses of mud, wattles, and thatch, and full of naked heathen. The Kavirondo are the nakedest of all African peoples and, it is said, the most moral. It put a great strain on Mrs. Diana; all that whole difficult anxious time, as it were detachedly, I could see her itching to get them into Mother Hubbards and cast-off Iowa pants.

Here, too, as the Major had promised, we found a holy of holies, rather a dreadful of dreadfuls, "taboo no end," its shadows cluttered with the hurlothrumbos of Diana's artistry. What puzzled me was their number. Why this appetite for experimentation? There was an uncertainty; one would think its effect on potential converts would be bad. Here, as in Ndua, Diana had contented himself at first with words and skyward gesticulations. Not for so long, however. Feeling the need of giving his concept of the cosmic "wearer" a substance much earlier, he had shut himself in with the work, literally — a fever of creation. We counted seventeen of the nameless "blobs," all done, we were told, in the seven days and nights before their maker had again cleared out. The villagers would hardly speak of him; only after spitting, their eyes averted, and in an undertone, would they mention him: "He of the Ring." Thereafter we were to hear of him only as "He of the Ring."

Leaving Suki, Major Wyeside turned us over (thankfully, I

warrant) to a native who told us his name was Charlie Kamba. He had spent some years in Nairobi, running for an Indian outfitter, and spoke English remarkably well. It was from him we learned, quite casually, when our modest eight-load *safari* was some miles on its way, that the primary object of our coming was non-existent. Hubert Diana was dead.

Dead nearly five weeks — a moon and a little — and buried in the mission church at Tara Hill.

Mission church! There was a poser for us. *Mission church?*

Well, then, Charlie Kamba gave us to know that he was paraphrasing in a large way suitable to our habits of thought. We shouldn't have understood *his* informant's "wizard house" or "house of the effigy."

I will say for Mrs. Diana that in the course of our halt of lugubrious amazement she shed tears. That some of them were not tears of unrealized relief it would be hardly natural to believe. She had desired loyally to find her husband, but when she should have found him — what? This problem, sturdily ignored so long, was now removed.

Turn back? Never! Now it would seem the necessity for pressing forward was doubled. In the scrub-fringed ravine of our halt the porters resumed their loads, the dust stood up again, the same caravan moved on. But how far it was now from being the same.

From that moment it took on, for me at least, a new character. It wasn't the news especially; the fact that Diana was dead had little to do with it. Perhaps it was simply that the new sense of something aimfully and cumulatively dramatic in our progress had to have a beginning, and that moment would do as well as the next.

Six villages: M'nann, Leika, Leikapo, Shamba, Little Tara, and Tara, culminating in the apotheosis of Tara Hill. Six stops for the night on the road it had cost Diana as many months to cover in his singular pilgrimage to his inevitable goal. Or in his flight to it. Yes, his stampede. Now the pipers at that four-day orgy of liberty on the *Platonic's* decks were at his heels for their pay. Now that his strength was failing, the hosts of loneliness were after him, creeping out of their dreadful magnitudes, the hounds of space. Over all that ground it seemed to me we were following him not by the world of hearsay but, as one follows a wounded animal making for its earth, by the droppings of his blood.

Our progress had taken on a pattern; it built itself with a dramatic artistry; it gathered suspense. As though it were a story at its most breathless places "continued in our next," and I a reader forgetting the road's weariness, the dust, the torment of insects never escaped, the inadequate food, I found myself hardly able to keep from running on ahead to reach the evening's village, to search out the inevitable repository of images left by the white stranger who had come and tarried there awhile and gone again.

More concrete and ever more concrete. The immemorial compromise with the human hunger for a symbol to see with the eyes, touch with the hands. Hierarchy after hierarchy of little mud effigies — one could see the necessity pushing the man. Out of the protoplasmic blobs of Ndua, Suki, even M'nann, at Leikapo Diana's concept of infinity (so pure in that halcyon epoch at sea), of categories nested within categories like Japanese boxes, of an over-creature wearing our cosmos like a trinket, unawares, had become a mass with legs to stand on and a real head. The shards scattered about in the filth of the hut there (as if in violence of despair) were still monstrosities, but with a sudden stride of concession their monstrousness was the monstrousness of lizard and turtle and crocodile. At Shamba there were dozens of huge-footed birds.

It is hard to be sure in retrospect, but I do believe that by the time we reached Little Tara I began to see the thing as a whole — the foetus, working out slowly, blindly, but surely, its evolution in the womb of fright. At Little Tara there was a change in the character of the exhibits; their numbers had diminished, their size had grown. There was a boar with tusks and a bull the size of a dog with horns, and on a tusk and on a horn an indentation left by a ring.

I don't believe Mrs. Diana got the thing at all. Toward the last she wasn't interested in the huts of relics; at Little Tara she wouldn't go near the place; she was "too tired." It must have been pretty awful, when you think of it, even if all she saw in them was the mud-pie play of a man reverted to a child.

There was another thing at Little Tara quite as momentous as the jump to boar and bull. Here at last a mask had been thrown aside. Here there had been no pretense of proselyting, no astronomical lectures, no doorway harangues. Straightway he had arrived (a fabulous figure already, long heralded), he had commandeered a house and shut himself up in it and there, mysterious, assiduous, he had remained three days and nights, eating nothing, but drinking gallons of the foul water they left in gourds outside his curtain of reeds. No one in the village had ever seen what he had done and left there. Now, candidly, those labours were for himself alone.

Here at last in Tara the moment of that confession had overtaken the fugitive. It was he, ill with fever and dying of nostalgia — not these naked black baboon men seen now as little more than blurs — who had to give the Beast of the Infinite a name and a shape. And more and more, not only a shape, but a *shapeliness*. From the instant when, no longer able to live alone with nothingness, he had given it a likeness in Ndua mud, and perceived that it was intolerable and fled its face, the turtles and distorted crocodiles of Leikapo and the birds of Shamba had become inevitable, and no less inevitable the Little Tara boar and bull. Another thing grows plain in retrospect: the reason why, done to death (as all the way they reported him) he couldn't die. He didn't dare to. Didn't dare to close his eyes.

It was at Little Tara we first heard of him as "Father Witch," a name come back, we were told, from Tara, where he had gone. I had heard it pronounced several times before it suddenly obtruded from the native context as actually two English words. That was what made it queer. It was something they must have picked up by rote, uncomprehending; something then they could have had from no lips but his own. When I repeated it after them with a better accent they pointed up toward the north, saying "Tara! Tara!" — their eagerness mingled with awe.

I shall never forget Tara as we saw it, after our last blistering scramble up a gorge, situated in the clear air on a slope belted with cedars. A mid-African stockade left by some blunder in an honest Colorado landscape, or a newer and bigger Vermont. Here at the top of our journey, black savages, their untidy *shambas,* the very Equator, all these seemed as incongruous as a Gothic cathedral in a Congo marsh. I wonder if Hubert Diana knew whither his instinct was guiding him on the long road of his journey here to die. . . .

He had died and he was buried, not in the village, but about half a mile distant, on the ridge; this we were given to know almost before we had arrived. There was no need to announce ourselves, the word of our coming had outrun us; the populace was at the gates.

"Our Father Witch! Our Father Witch!" They knew what we were after; the funny parrot-wise English stood out from the clack and clatter of their excited speech. "Our Father Witch! Ay! Ay!" With a common eagerness they gesticulated at the hilltop beyond the cedars.

Certainly here was a change. No longer the propitiatory spitting, the averted eyes, the uneasy whispering allusion to him who had passed that way: here in Tara they would shout him from the housetops, with a kind of civic pride.

We learned the reason for this on our way up the hill. It was because they were his chosen, the initiate.

We made the ascent immediately, against the village's advice. It was near evening; the return would be in the dark; it was bad lion country; wouldn't to-morrow morning do? . . . No, it wouldn't do the widow. Her face was set. . . . And so, since we were resolved to go, the village went with us, armed with spears and rattles and drums. Charlie Kamba walked beside us, sifting the information a hundred were eager to give.

These people were proud, he said, because their wizard was more powerful than all the wizards of all the other villages "in the everywhere together." If he cared to he could easily knock down all the other villages in the "everywhere," destroying all the people and all the cattle. If he cared to he could open his mouth and swallow the sky and the stars. But Tara he had chosen. Tara he would protect. He made their mealies to grow and their cattle to multiply.

I protested, "But he is *dead* now!"

Charlie Kamba made signs of deprecation. I discerned that he was far from clear about the thing himself.

Yes, he temporized, this Father Witch was dead, quite dead. On the other hand, he was up there. On the other hand, he would never die. He was longer than for ever. Yes, quite true, he was dead and buried under the pot.

I gave it up. "How did he die?"

Well, he came to this village of Tara very suffering, very sick. The dead man who walked. His face was very sad. Very eaten. Very frightened. He came to this hill. So he lived here for two full moons, very hot, very eaten, very dead. These men made him a house as he commanded them, also a stockade. In the house he was very quiet, very dead, making magic two full moons. Then he came out and they that were waiting saw him. He had made the magic, and the magic had made him well. His face was kind. He was happy. He was full fed. He was full fed, these men said, without any eating. Yes, they carried up to him very fine food, because they were full of wonder and some fear, but he did not eat any of it. Some water he drank. So, for two days and the night between them, he continued sitting in the gate of the stockade, very happy, very full fed. He told these people very much about their wizard, who is bigger than everywhere and longer than for ever and can, if he cares to, swallow the sky and stars. From time to time, however, ceasing to talk to these people, he got to his knees and talked in his own strange tongue to Our Father Witch, his eyes held shut. When he had done this just at sunset of the second day he fell forward on his face. So he remained that night. The next day these men took him into the house and buried him under the pot. On the other hand, Our Father Witch is longer than for ever. He remains there still. . . .

The first thing I saw in the hut's interior was the earthen pot at the northern end, wrong-side-up on the ground. I was glad I had preceded Mrs. Diana. I walked across and sat down on it carelessly, hoping so that her afflicted curiosity might be led astray. It gave me the oddest feeling, though, to think of what was there beneath my nonchalant sitting-portion — aware as I was of the Kavirondo burial of a great man — up to the neck in mother earth, and the rest of him left out in the dark of the pot for the undertakings of the ants. I hoped his widow wouldn't wonder about that inverted vessel of clay.

I needn't have worried. Her attention was arrested otherwheres. I shall not forget the look of her face, caught above me in the red shaft of sundown entering the western door, as she gazed at the last and the largest of the Reverend Hubert Diana's gods. That long, long cheek of hers, buffeted by sorrow, startled now, and mortified. Not till that moment, I believe, had she comprehended the steps of mud images she had been following for what they were, the steps of idolatry.

For my part, I wasn't startled. Even before we started up the hill, knowing that her husband had dared to die here, I could have told her pretty much what she would find.

This overlord of the cosmic categories that he had fashioned (at last) in his own image sat at the other end of the red-streaked house upon a bench — a throne? — of mud. Diana had been no artist. An ovoid two-eyed head, a cylindrical trunk, two arms, two legs, that's all. But indubitably man, man-size. Only one finger of one of the hands had been done with much care. It wore an opal, a two-dollar stone from Mexico, set in a silver ring. This was the hand that was lifted, and over it the head was bent.

I've said Diana was no artist. I'll take back the words. The figure was crudeness itself, but in the relation between that bent head and that lifted hand there was something which was something else. A sense of scrutiny one would have said no genius of mud could ever have conveyed. An attitude of interest centred in that bauble, intense and static, breathless and eternal all in one — penetrating to its bottom atom, to the last electron, to a hill upon it, and to a two-legged mite about to die. Marking (yes, I'll swear to the incredible) the sparrow's fall.

The magic was made. The road that had commenced with the blobs of Ndua — the same that commenced with our hairy ancestors listening to the night wind in their caves — was run.

And from here Diana, of a sudden happy, of a sudden looked after, "full fed," had walked out ——

But no; I couldn't stand that mortified sorrow on the widow's face any longer. She had to be made to see. I said it aloud:

"From here, Mrs. Diana, your husband walked out —— "

"He had sunk to idolatry. *Idolatry!*"

"To the bottom, yes. And come up its whole history again. And from here he walked out into the sunshine to kneel and talk with 'Our Father Which ——' "

She got it. She caught it. I wish you could have seen the light going up those long, long cheeks as she got it:

"Our Father which art in Heaven, Hallowed be Thy Name!"

We went down hill in the darkness, convoyed by a vast rattling of gourds and beating of goat-hide drums.

NADINE GORDINER

The Bride of Christ

Lyndall Berger, at sixteen, wrote to her parents for permission to be confirmed.

"Are you mad?" Sidney's gaze was a pair of outspread arms, stopping his wife short whichever way she might turn.

"Well, I know. But it never enters your mind that for someone — I'm not saying for *her* — it could be necessary; real, I mean. When one says 'no,' one must concede that. Otherwise she must put the refusal down to rationalist prejudice. You see what I mean?"

"Saved them all the abracadabra at the synagogue for this. Mumbo jumbo for abracadabra."

It was Shirley who had agreed when the child went to boarding school that she could go to church with the other girls if she felt like it — just to see what it was all about. She bought her, at the same time, a Penguin on comparative religion; in the holidays she could read James Parkes on the origins of Judaism and Christianity, right-hand lower bookshelf near the blue lamp. Shirley did not know whether the child had ever read either; you were in the same position as you were with sex: you gave them the facts, and you left an unspoken, unanswerable question. How does it feel to want to perform this strange act? How does it feel to have faith?

"It's like cutting her skirts up to her thigh. She wants to be confirmed because her friends are going to be. The answer is no."

His wife's face winced in anticipation of the impact of this sort of dismissal. "Of course it's no. But we must show her the respect of giving her the proper reasons. I'll talk to her when she's home next Sunday."

Shirley had meant to take her daughter for a walk in the veld, but it wasn't necessary because Sidney and Peter, their other child, went off to play golf anyway. Shirley was not slow to take a stand on the one ground that stood firm beneath her feet. "You've been going to church for over a year now. I suppose you haven't failed to notice that all those nicely dressed ladies and gentlemen of the congregation are white? A church isn't a cinema, you know — I say this because we get used to seeing only white people in public places like that, and it's quite understandable that one begins to take it for granted. But a church is different, you know that; the church preaches brotherhood, and there's no excuse. Except prejudice. They pray to God, and they take the body of Christ into their mouths, but they don't want to do it next to a black man. You must have thought about it often."

"I think about it all the time," the girl said. They were peeling mushrooms; she didn't do it well; she broke off bits of the cap along with the skin she rolled back, but her mother didn't complain this time.

"That's why Sidney and I don't go to synagogue or church or anything — one of the reasons. Daddy wouldn't belong to any religion wherever he lived — that you know — but perhaps I might want to if I lived anywhere else, not here. I couldn't sit with them in their churches or synagogues here."

"I know." Lyndall did not look up.

"I wonder how you feel about this." No answer. Shirley felt there should be no necessity to spell it out, but to force the child to speak, she said, "How can you want to join the establishment of the Church when there's a color bar there?"

"Well, yes, I know —" Lyndall said.

Her mother said of the mushroom stalks, "Just break them off; I'll use them for soup."

They returned to the silence between them, but a promising silence, with something struggling through it.

"I think about it every time I'm in church — I'm always — but it's got nothing to do with Christ, Mummy. It's not his fault" — she paused with shame for the schoolgirl phrasing before this woman, her mother, who inevitably had the advantage of adult articulacy — "not Christ's fault that people are hypocrites."

"Yes, of course, that's the point I'm trying to make for you. I can understand anyone being attracted to the Christian ethic, to Christ's teaching, to the idea of following him. But why join the Church; it's done such awful things in his name."

"That's got nothing to do with Christ."

"You associate yourself with them! The moment you get yourself confirmed and join the Church, you belong along with it all, from the Crusaders and the Spanish Inquisition to the good Christian Nazis, and the good Christians of the Dutch Reformed Church who sprinkle pious sentiments over the color bar the way the Portuguese bishops used to baptize slaves before they were shipped from West Africa — you belong along with them just the way you do in church with the nice ladies in smart hats who wouldn't want a black child sitting beside theirs in school."

Lyndall was afraid of her mother's talk; often the constructions she had balanced in her mind out of her own ideas fell down before her mother's talk like the houses made of sticks and jacaranda feathers that used to turn to garden rubbish beneath the foot of an unrecognizing grown-up.

She was going to be quite good-looking (Shirley thought so), but the conflict of timidity and determination gave her the heavy-jawed look of a certain old uncle, a failure in the family, whom Shirley remembered from her own childhood.

"What about Garth and Nibs?"

The child made the statement. The Lellands, ex-missionaries who had both been put under government ban for their activities as members of the Liberal Party, were among the Bergers' closest friends.

"Yes, Garth and Nibs, and Father Huddleston and Bishop Reeves and Crowther and a lot of other names. Of course there are Anglicans and Catholics and Methodists who don't preach brotherhood and forget it when it comes to a black face. But the fact is that they're the rarities. Odd men out. The sort of people you'll be worshiping Christ with every Sunday are the people who see no wrong in their black brothers' having to carry a pass. The same sort of people who didn't see anything wrong in your great-grandparents' having to live in a ghetto in Galicia. The same people who kept going to church in Germany on Sundays while the Jews were being shoveled into gas ovens."

She watched her daughter's face for the expression that knew *that* was coming; couldn't be helped, it had to be dragged up, again and again and again and again and again — like Lear's "nevers" — no matter how sick of it everyone might be.

But the child's face was naked.

"Darling" — the words found release suddenly, in helplessness — "I really can understand how you feel. I'm not just talking; I can tell you that if I had a religion at all it could only be Christ's; I've never been able to understand why the Jews didn't accept him, it's so logical that his thinking should have been the culmination — but I know I couldn't become a Christian, couldn't . . ."

The child didn't help her.

"Because of *that*. And the other things. That go with it. It's like having one drop of colored blood in your veins. You'd always have to admit it, I mean, wouldn't you? You'd always want to tell people first. Everything'd have to begin from there. Well, it's just the same if you're a Jew. People like us — color and race, it doesn't mean a damn thing to me, but it can only not mean a thing if I begin from there, from having it known that I'm Jewish. I don't choose to belong with the ladies who separate the meat and the milk dishes and wear their Sunday best to synagogue, but I can't not choose the people who were barred from the universities — they were, just like the Africans, here — and killed by the Germans

— you understand?" Her voice dropped from an apologetic rise; she hadn't wanted to bring it in, again. Lyndall was rubbing rolls of dirt on her sweating hands. She blinked jerkily now and then as the words pelted her. "And you, you belong along with that too, d'you understand, you'll always belong with it. Doesn't matter if you're confirmed a hundred times over. And another thing — it's all part of the same thing really. If you were to become a Christian, there would always be the suspicion in people's minds that you'd done it for social reasons."

In her innocence, the child opened her lips on a gleam of tooth, and frowned, puzzled.

Shirley felt ashamed at what was once trivial and urgently important. "Clubs and so on. Even certain schools. They don't want to admit Jews. Oh, it's a bore to talk about it. When you think what Africans are debarred from. But at the same time — one wants *all* the pinpricks, one must show them one won't evade a single one. How can I explain — pride, it's a kind of pride. I couldn't turn my back on it."

The child moved her head slowly and vehemently in understanding, as she used to do, near tears, when she had had a dressing-down. "Lyndall," her mother said, "you'd have to be a real Christian, an every-minute-of-the-day, every-day-of-the-week Christian, before I could think of letting you be converted. You'd have to take all this on you. You'd have to know that the person kneeling beside you in church might make some remark about Jews one day, and you wouldn't be able to let it pass, like a Christian; you'd have to say, I'm Jewish. I'd want you to take the kicks from both sides. It would be the only way."

"Oh, but I will, I will, I promise you, Mummy!" The child jumped clumsily, forgetting she was almost grown-up, forgetting her size, and gave her mother the hard kisses of childhood that landed on cheek and chin. The bowl of mushrooms turned over and spun loudly like a top coming to rest, and scrabbling for the mushrooms, looking up from under the hair that fell forward over her face, she talked: "Father Byrd absolutely won't allow you to be confirmed until you're sure you're ready — I've had talks with him three times — he comes to the school on Thursdays — and I know I'm ready, I feel it. I promise you, Mummy."

Shirley was left with the empty bowl; she urgently wanted to speak, to claim what had been taken out of her hands; but all she did was remove, by pressure of the pads of her fingers, the grit in the fungus dew at the bottom.

Of course Lyndall had to be baptized, too. They hadn't realized it, or perhaps the child had wanted to break the whole business gently, one piece of preposterousness at a time. She had been named originally for that free spirit in Olive Schreiner's book, a shared feeling for which had been one of the signs that brought her parents together. Her mother attended both the baptismal and confirmation ceremonies; it was understood that Sidney, while granting his daughter her kind of freedom, would not be expected to be present. For the confirmation Lyndall had to have a sleeveless white dress with a long-sleeved bolero; all the other girls were having them made like that. "So's you can wear the dress for parties afterwards," she said.

"One never wears these dresses for anything afterwards," said her mother. Eighteen years in a plastic bag, the zipper made tarnish marks on the wedding dress.

Lyndall also had to have a veil, plain muslin, like a nursing sister's. It was even held in place with bronze bobby pins.

"The Bride of Christ," said Sidney when, trying it on, she had left the room. At least he had managed not to say anything while she was there; Shirley looked up for a second, as if he had spoken to her thoughts. But he was alone in his own.

"She's not going into a nunnery," she said.

Yet why did she feel such a cheat with him over this thing? He could have stopped the child if he'd been absolutely convinced, absolutely adamant. The heavy father. How much distaste he had — they had — for the minor tyrannies. . . It was all very well to set children free, he wouldn't compromise himself to himself by accepting that he might have to use the power of authority to keep them that way.

Lyndall was weeping when the bishop in his purple robes called her name and blessed her in the school chapel. The spasm on the rather large child's face under the ugly veil as she arose from her knees produced a nervous automatic counterspasm within her mother; the child was one of those who hadn't cried beyond the grazed-knees stage. Shirley stirred on her hard chair as if about to speak to someone, even to giggle . . . but she was alone: on the one side, somebody's grandmother with a pearl earring shaking very slightly; on the other, a parent in dark gray hopsack with no gap between trouser and sock. Afterward there was tea and cake and an air of mild congratulation in the school hall. Meeting over a communal sugar bowl, Shirley and another woman smiled at each other in the manner of people who do not know one another's names. "A big day in their lives, isn't it? And just as well to get it over with so they can settle down to work before the exams, I was just saying . . ." Shirley smiled and murmured the appropriate half phrases. The white dresses swooped in and out among the mothers and fathers. Bobbing breasts and sturdy hams, or the thin waists and blindly nosing little peaks just touching the flat bodices, but nubile, nubile. That was Sidney's explanation for the whole thing: awakening sexuality, finding an emotional outlet; they do not love Christ, they are in love with him, a symbolic male figure, and indeed, what about Father Whatnot with his pale, clean priest's hands, appearing every Thursday among three hundred females?

Father Byrd was gaily introducing the bishop to a parent in a blue swansdown hat. The bishop had disrobed, and appeared in the assembly like an actor who has taken off his splendid costume and makeup. The confirmants were displaying presents that lay in cotton wool within hastily torn tissue paper; they raced about to give each other the fancy cards they had bought. Lyndall, with a deep, excited smile, found her mother. They kissed, and Lyndall clung to her. "Bless you, darling, bless you, bless you," Shirley said. Lyndall kept lifting her hair off her forehead with the back of a mannered hand, and saying with pleased, embarrassed casualness, "What chaos! Could you see us shaking? I thought I'd *never* — we could hardly get up the steps! Did you see my *veil?* Roseann's was down to her nose! What chaos! Did you see how we all bunched together? Father Byrd told us a million times . . ." Her eyes were all around the room, as if acknowledging applause. She showed her mother her cards, with the very faint suggestion of defiance, not used but at the ready; but there was no need — with heads at an angle so that both could see at the same time, they looked at the doggerel in gilt script and the tinsel-nimbused figures as if they had never wrinkled their noses in amusement at greeting-card sentimentality. Shirley said, "Darling, instead of giving you some little" (she was going to say "cross or something," because every other girl seemed to have been given a gold crucifix and chain), "some present for yourself, we're sending a donation to the African Children's Feeding Scheme in your name. Don't you think that makes sense?"

Lyndall agreed before her mother had finished speaking: "That's a much better idea." Her face was vivid. She had never looked quite like that before; charming, movingly charming. Must be the tears and excitement, bringing blood to the surface of the skin. An emotional surrogate, Sidney would have said, if Shirley had told him about it. But it was something she wanted to keep; and so she said nothing, telling the others at home only about the splendor of the bishop's on-stage appearance, and the way the girls who were not confirmants hung about outside the school hall, hoping for leftover sandwiches. Peter grinned — he had disliked boarding school so much that they had had to take him away. Beyond this, they had had no trouble with him at all. He certainly had not been bothered by any religious phase; he was a year older than Lyndall, and as pocket and odd-job money would allow, was slowly building a boat in a friend's backyard.

When Lyndall was home for a weekend she got up while the rest of the house was still asleep on Sunday mornings and went to Communion at the church down the road. It was her own affair; no one remarked on it one way or another. Meeting her with wine on her breath and the slightly stiff face that came from the early morning air her mother, still in a dressing gown, sometimes made a gentle joke: "Boozing before breakfast, what a thing," and kissed the fresh, cool cheek. Lyndall smiled faintly and was gone upstairs, to come clattering down changed into the trousers and shirt that was the usual weekend dress of the family. She ate with concentration an enormous breakfast: all the things she didn't get at school.

Before her conversion, she and Shirley had often talked about religion, but now when Shirley happened to be reading Simone Weil's letters and told Lyndall something of her life and thought, the girl had the inattentive smile, the hardly patient inclinations of the head, of someone too polite to rebuff an intrusion on privacy. Well, Shirley realized that she perhaps read too much into this; Simone Weil's thinking was hardly on the level of a girl of sixteen; Lyndall probably couldn't follow.

Or perhaps it was because Simone Weil was Jewish. If Lyndall had shown more interest, her mother certainly would have explained to her that she hadn't brought up the subject of Simone Weil because of *that,* Lyndall must believe her; but given the lack of interest, what was the point?

During the Christmas holidays Lyndall went to a lot of parties and overslept on several Sunday mornings. Sometimes she went to a service later in the day, and then usually asked Shirley to drive her to church: "It's absolutely boiling, trekking there in this heat." On Christmas morning she was up and off to Mass at dawn, and when she came back, the family had the usual present-giving in the dining room, with the servants, Ezekiel and Margaret and Margaret's little daughter, Winnie, and constant interruptions as the dustmen, the milkman, and various hangers-on called at the kitchen door for their "bonsella," their Christmas tip. The Bergers had always celebrated Christmas, partly because they had so many friends who were not Jews who inevitably included the Bergers in their own celebrations, and partly because, as Sidney said, holidays, saints' days — whatever the occasion, it didn't matter — were necessary to break up the monotony of daily life. He pointed out, apropos Christmas, that among the dozens of Christmas cards the Bergers got, there was always one from an Indian Muslim friend. Later in the day the family were expected at a Christmas lunch and swimming party at the Trevor-Pearses'. After a glass of champagne in the sun, Shirley suddenly said to Sidney, "I'm afraid that our daughter's the only Christian of the lot who's been to church today," and he said, with the deadpan, young-wise face that she had always liked so much, "What d'you expect, don't you know the Jews always overdo it?"

The Bergers thought they would go to the Kruger Park over the Easter weekend. As children grew older, there were fewer things all the members of a family could enjoy together, and this sort of little trip was a safe choice for a half-term holiday. When they told Peter, he said, "Fine, fine," but before Shirley could write to Lyndall, there was a letter from her saying she hoped there wasn't "anything on" at half term, because she and her school friends had the whole weekend planned, with a party on the Thursday night when they came home, and a picnic on the Vaal on Easter Monday, and she must do some shopping in town on the Saturday morning. Since Lyndall was the one who was at boarding school, there was the feeling that family plans ought to be designed to fit in with her inclinations rather than anyone else's. If Lyndall wasn't keen, should they stay at home, after all? "Fine, fine," Peter said. It didn't seem to matter to him one way or the other. And Sidney, everyone knew, privately thought April still too hot a month for the Game Reserve. "We can go at our leisure in the August holidays," he said, made expansive and considerate by the reprieve. "Yes, of course, fine," Peter said. He had told Shirley that he and his friend expected to finish the boat and get it down for a tryout in Durban during August.

A friend at school had cut Lyndall's hair, and she came out of school as conscious of this as a puppy cleverly carrying a shoe in its mouth. Her mother liked the look of her, and Sidney said "Thank God" in comment on the fact that she hadn't been able to see out of her eyes before, and whatever reaction there was from her brother was elicited behind closed doors, like all the other exchanges between brother and sister in the sudden and casual intimacy that seemed to grow up between them, apparently over a record that Lyndall had borrowed and brought home. They played it over and over on Thursday afternoon, shut in Lyndall's room.

Lyndall's head was done up like a parcel, with transparent sticky tape holding strands of hair in place on her forehead and cheeks; she gave her fingernails a coating like that of a cheap pearl necklace and then took it off again. She had to be delivered to the house where the party was being held by seven, and explained that she would be brought home by someone else; she knew how her mother and father disliked having to sit up late to come and fetch her. Her mother successfully prevented herself from saying, "How late will it be?" — what was the use of making these ritual responses in an unacknowledged ceremony of initiation to adult life? Tribal Africans took the young into the bush for a few weeks, and got it all over at once. Those free from the rites of primitive peoples repeated plaintive remarks, tags of a litany of instruction half but never quite forgotten, from one generation to the next.

Lyndall came home very late indeed, and didn't get up until eleven next morning. Her brother had long gone off to put in a full day's work on the boat. It was hot for early autumn, and the girl lay on the drying grass in her pink gingham bikini, sunbathing. Shirley said to her, "Isn't it awful, I can't do that anymore. Just lie. I don't know when it went." Whenever the telephone rang behind them in the house, Lyndall got up at once. Her laughter and bursts of intense; sibilant, confidential talk now sounded, now were cut off, as Ezekiel and Margaret went about the house and opened or closed a door or window. Between calls, Lyndall came out and dropped back to the grass. Now and then she hummed an echo of last night's party; the tune disappeared into her thoughts again. Sometimes a smile, surfacing, made her open her eyes, and she would tell Shirley some incident, tearing off a fragment from the sounds, shapes, and colors that were turning in the red dark of her closed lids.

After lunch her mother asked whether she could summon the energy for a walk down to the shops — "You'll have an early night tonight, anyway." They tried to buy some fruit, but of course even the Portuguese greengrocers were closed on Good Friday.

As they came back into the house, Sidney said, "Someone phoned twice. A boy with a French name, Jean-something, Frebert, Brebert?"

Lyndall opened her eyes in pantomime astonishment; last night's mascara had worked its way out as a black dot in the inner corner of one. Then a look almost of pain, a closing away of suspicion, took her face. "I don't believe it!"

"The first time I'd just managed to get Lemmy down on the bathroom floor," said Sidney. The dog had an infected ear and had to be captured with cunning for his twice-daily treatment. "You won't get within a mile of him again today."

"Jean? He's from Canada, somebody's cousin they brought along last night. Did he say he'd phone again, or what? He didn't leave a number?"

"He did not."

She went up to her room and shut the door and played the record. But when the telephone rang she was somehow alert to it through the noisy music and was swift to answer before either Shirley or Sidney moved to put aside their books. The low light voice she used for talking to boys did not carry the way the exaggeratedly animated one that was for girls did. But by the time Shirley had reached the end of the chapter they had heard her run upstairs.

Then she appeared in the doorway and smiled in on the pair. "What d'you know, there's another party. This boy Jean's just asked me to go. It's in a stable, he says; everyone's going in denims."

"Someone you met last night?"

"*Jean*. The one Daddy spoke to. You know."

"Such gaiety," said Sidney. "Well, he's not one to give up easily."

"Won't you be exhausted?"

But Shirley understood that Lyndall quite rightly wouldn't even answer that. She gave a light, patronizing laugh. "He says he wanted to ask me last night, but he was scared."

"Will you be going before or after dinner?" said Shirley.

"Picking me up at a quarter past seven."

In Shirley's silences a room became like a scene enclosed in a glass paperweight, waiting for the touch that would set the snow whirling. The suburban church bells began to ring, muffled by the walls, dying away in waves, a ringing in the ears.

"I'll give you a scrambled egg."

Lyndall came down to eat in her dressing gown, straight out of the bath: "I'm ready, Ma." Sidney was still reading, his drink fizzling flat, scarcely touched, on the floor beside him. Shirley sat down at the coffee table where Lyndall's tray was and slowly smoked, and slowly rose and went to fetch the glass she had left somewhere else. Her movements seemed reluctant. She held the glass and watched the child eat. She said, "I notice there's been no talk of going to church today."

Lyndall gave her a keen look across a slice of bread and butter she was just biting into.

"I woke up too late this morning."

"I know. But there are other services. All day. It's Good Friday, the most important day in the year."

Lyndall put the difficulty in her mother's hands as she used to give over the knotted silver chain of her locket to be disentangled by adult patience and a pin. "I meant to go to this evening's."

"Yes," said Shirley, "but you are going to a party."

"Oh, Mummy."

"Only seven months since you got yourself confirmed, and you can go to a party on Good Friday. Just another party; like all the others you go to."

A despairing fury sprang up so instantly in the girl that her father looked around as if a stone had hurtled into the room. "I knew it. I knew you were thinking that! As if I don't feel terrible about it! I've felt terrible all day! You don't have to come and tell me it's Good Friday!" And tears shook in her eyes at the shame.

Peter had come in, a presence of wood glue and sweat, not unpleasant, in the room. Under his rough eyebrows, bridged by the redness of an adolescent skin irritation, he stared a moment and then seemed at once to understand everything. He sat quietly on a footstool.

"The most important day in the year for a Christian. Even the greengrocers closed, you saw—"

"I just knew you were thinking that about me, I knew it." Lyndall's voice was stifled in tears and anger. "And how do you think I feel when I have to go to church alone on Sunday mornings? All on my own. Nobody knows me there. And that atmosphere when I walk into the house and you're all here. How d'you think I *feel?*" She stopped to sob dramatically, and yet sincerely; her mother said nothing, but her father's head inclined to one side, as one offers comfort without asking the cause of pain. "And when you said that about the present—everyone else just got one, no fuss. Even while I was being confirmed I could feel you sitting there, and I knew what you were thinking—how d'you think it is, for me?"

"Good God," Shirley said in the breathy voice of amazement, "I came to the confirmation in complete sincerity. You're being unfair. Once I'd accepted that you wanted to be a real Christian, not a social one—"

"You see? You see? You're always at me—"

"At you? This is the first time the subject's ever come up. When've I ever said a word?"

The girl looked at them blindly. "I know I'm a bad Christian! I listen to them in church, and it just seems a lot of rubbish. I pray, I pray every night—" Desperation stopped her mouth.

"Lyndall, you say you want Christ, and I believe you," said Shirley.

The girl was enraged. "Don't say it! You don't, you don't, you never did."

"Yet you make yourself guilty and unhappy by going out dancing on the day that Christ was crucified."

"Oh, why can't you just leave her alone?" It was Peter, his head lifted from his arms. His mother took the accusation like a blow in the chest.

Sidney spoke for the first time. "What's the matter with you?"

"Just leave her alone," Peter said. "Making plans, asking questions. Just leave people alone, can't you?"

Sidney knew that he was not the one addressed, and so he answered. "I don't know what you're getting hysterical about, Peter. No one's even mentioned your name."

"Well, we talk about you plenty, behind your back, to our friends, I can tell you." His lips pulled with a trembling, triumphant smile. The two children did not look at each other.

"Coffee or a glass of milk?" Shirley said into the silence, standing up.

Lyndall didn't answer, but said, "Well, I'm not going. You can tell him I'm sick or dead or something. Anything. When he comes."

"I suggest you ring up and make some excuse," said Shirley.

The girl gestured it away; her fingers were limply twitching. "Don't even know where to get him. He'll be on his way now. He'll think I'm mad."

"I'll tell him. I'm going to tell him just exactly what happened," said Peter, looking past his mother.

She went and stood in the kitchen because there was nobody there. She was listening for the voices in the living room, and yet there was nothing she wanted to hear. Sidney found her. He had brought Lyndall's tray. "I don't understand it," he said. "If the whole thing's half-forgotten already, why push her into it again? For heaven's sake, what are you, an evangelist or something? Do you have to take it on yourself to make converts? Since when the missionary spirit? For God's sake, let's leave well alone. I mean, anyone would think, listening to you in there—"

His wife stood against the dresser with her shoulders hunched, pulling the points of her collar up over her chin. He leaned behind her and tightened the dripping tap. She was quiet. He put his hand on her cheek. "Never mind. High-handed little devils. Enough of this God-business for today."

He went upstairs and she returned to the living room. Lyndall was blowing her nose and pressing impatiently at the betrayal of tears that still kept coming, an overflow, to her brilliant, puffy eyes.

"You don't know how to get hold of the boy?" Shirley said.

There was a pause. "I told you."

"Don't you know the telephone number?"

"I'm not going to phone Clare Pirie—he's her cousin."

"It would be so rude to let him come for you for nothing," said Shirley. Nobody spoke. "Lyndall, I think you'd better go." She stopped, and then went on in a tone carefully picking a way through presumption, "I mean, one day is like another. And these dates are arbitrary, anyway, nobody really knows when it was, for sure—the ritual observance isn't really the thing—is it?—"

"Look what I look like," said the girl.

"Well, just go upstairs now"—the cadence was simple, sensible, comforting, like a nursery rhyme — "and wash your face with cold water, and brush your hair, and put on a bit of makeup."

"Well, I suppose so. Don't feel much like dancing," the girl added, offhand, in a low voice to her mother, and the two faces shared, for a moment, a family likeness of doubt that the boy Peter did not see.